Ludere Latine II

by Paul OßRien

coordinated with Latina Christiana II

Additional Discounted Copies of Ludere Latine II

If you purchased this book NEW:
You may order additional bound Ludere Latine II books online for less than the
cost of copying. To order additional discounted books, go to
www.MemoriaPress.com/copy

Ludere Latine II: Latin Games & Puzzles
by Paul OBrien

© 2005 Memoria Press
ISBN #: 1-930953-98-4

Memoria Press
www.memoriapress.com

CONTENTS

INTRODUCTION

This is the second volume of Ludere Latine, the book of Latin word games from Memoria Press. It is coordinated with the Memoria Press Latin course Latina Christiana II. Each lesson of Ludere Latine II uses the vocabulary of the corresponding lesson of Latina Christiana II.

This book contains seven kinds of word games.

The first game is Word Search. The Latin words concealed in the matrix are identified by the clues in English. Some clues are simple definitions. Some require specific grammatical forms.

The second game is Lacunae, which means "holes" in Latin. The point of the game is to fill in the items missing from each table.

The third game is Derivatives Crossword. The clues are Latin words taken from the vocabulary lists of Latina Christiana II. You fill the crossword with English derivatives of these words.

The fourth game is Grammar Crossword. The clues are English words. You fill the crossword with equivalent Latin words in the required grammatical forms.

The fifth game is Transformer. The point of the game is to convert one Latin sentence into another by replacing one word at a time. A full explanation of this game along with examples is found on page 18, right before the first instance of the game.

The sixth game is Parse Strings. The point is to match each word on the left with a parsing on the right. This game can be tricky, so pay close attention to such things as gender, number, case, person and tense.

The seventh game is Match Up. The column on the left contains English words related to the Latin words in Latina Christiana II. For each of these, you find a word in the right column that best matches it. The criterion for a match may be similar meaning, opposite meaning or associated meaning.

LESSON 1

WORD SEARCH

```
L  N  J  S  E  D  E  B  A  M  U  S  G  P  R  L
M  L  U  T  Q  O  N  A  R  R  A  M  U  S  A  W
X  B  D  I  A  R  C  Q  F  F  J  R  K  U  M  T
Z  N  I  M  G  L  S  C  N  R  V  N  D  Q  N  K
N  T  C  E  V  R  U  L  U  J  M  A  V  U  Q  M
R  N  A  T  K  N  M  B  S  P  B  C  B  T  M  O
T  A  B  I  T  Z  I  I  M  A  A  A  P  Y  Y  V
I  B  A  S  T  B  B  H  M  A  D  B  W  L  X  E
B  A  M  D  J  A  A  L  R  P  X  M  A  M  B  B
E  V  U  T  T  B  N  C  P  O  F  M  O  T  B  A
C  A  S  C  E  Y  G  J  Q  R  M  F  F  N  G  S
O  L  E  B  M  L  U  B  Y  T  F  M  P  M  E  T
D  P  O  K  R  K  P  R  A  L  N  P  Q  Q  T
S  K  S  I  B  A  R  A  P  T  L  J  M  G  B  P
Q  H  T  I  B  E  D  I  V  I  C  L  A  M  A  T
N  T  E  R  R  E  N  T  T  S  U  M  E  B  U  J
```

she will teach	it was seizing
I will have	you will prepare
we order	you (pl.) carry
we were judging	we will fight
I was praising	we were sitting
they were washing	you will look at
it warns	they frighten
you were moving	you (pl.) fear
we are telling	she will see
he is walking	she shouts
they will give	

possum	
	possunt

habes	habetis

	parabimus
parabis	

timebat	timebant

Derivatives Crossword

Across

2. adoro (9)
5. habeo (5)
6. libero (8)
7. voco (10)
13. specto (11)
14. timeo (10)
15. doceo (8)
17. habito (7)
20. paro (11)
21. amo (7)
22. video (7)

Down

1. navigo (9)
3. clamo (6)
4. sedeo (9)
8. ambulo (9)
9. oro (7)
10. occupo (10)
11. moneo (7)
12. judico (7)
16. laboro (9)
18. moveo (6)
19. narro (7)

Grammar Crossword

Across

1. you fight (6)
3. I will fear (6)
6. it frees (7)
7. we will prevent (12)
9. we will seize (11)
12. they do wash (6)
13. you (pl.) were giving (7)
14. you see (5)
17. they will love (7)
18. you (pl.) carry (8)
20. they praise (7)
22. we will walk (11)
25. I was living in (9)
29. you (pl.) do frighten (8)
31. he will live in (9)
33. they will overcome (10)
34. I am able (6)
36. they will move (8)
37. we can (8)
39. you will adore (8)
41. I was sitting (7)
42. I will tell (7)
43. they will warn (8)
44. I was walking (9)
45. you (pl.) will call (9)

Down

1. I will prepare (6)
2. she was adoring (8)
4. you (pl.) are (5)
5. we judge (9)
6. it was working (9)
8. it can (6)
10. we will be shouting (10)
11. I was moving (7)
15. I was preparing (7)
16. I was calling (7)
19. you fear (5)
21. you (pl.) will have (9)
23. they are (4)
24. they were sailing (10)
26. she is looking at (7)
27. I will order (6)
28. they owe (6)
30. he will teach (7)
32. you are addressing (8)
33. we will look at (11)
35. I am (3)
38. we were praying (8)
40. they give (4)

Match Up

document	house
inhabit	computer
laudable	fearless
monitor	silent
portable	wow
timid	court
justice	siren
vocal	praiseworthy
ambulance	paper
navigation	immovable
exclamation	audio
video	sailing

WORD SEARCH

```
I  H  I  M  D  T  Y  N  P  R  T  M  M  M  H  K  I
P  U  E  L  L  I  S  F  C  A  Q  U  A  E  K  J  N
V  F  T  K  Q  L  M  A  A  C  K  M  I  M  N  K  S
X  X  L  G  N  V  C  N  U  U  M  X  L  N  O  L  F  U
Q  J  R  N  M  U  I  L  R  D  A  N  U  R  Y  I  L
R  R  D  H  T  U  P  C  A  A  R  M  C  I  F  L  A
W  P  W  R  K  A  R  T  T  J  R  D  E  A  E  I  R
K  Z  O  V  S  F  I  A  O  O  Q  O  P  M  N  A  U
D  F  W  F  R  V  E  N  R  G  R  R  H  S  E  M  M
E  A  L  L  E  T  S  M  J  R  E  I  I  L  S  K  T
Y  R  T  J  G  K  A  J  I  H  E  L  I  S  T  N  H
D  P  T  L  V  S  I  V  F  N  V  T  A  S  R  Y  T
K  K  P  O  L  I  R  N  K  I  A  N  T  X  A  V  N
K  H  B  J  R  I  O  S  S  R  I  R  E  A  N  U  L
M  I  K  R  I  V  L  O  V  G  N  A  U  T  I  S  R
S  T  V  U  F  J  G  N  E  M  V  W  M  M  J  P  X
R  P  T  B  C  W  N  R  Y  V  T  M  H  B  F  D  K
```

water (dat.)	hours (gen.)	queens (acc.)
faults (acc.)	islands (gen.)	forests (abl.)
I (nom.)	moon (gen.)	stars (nom.)
rumor (acc.)	memory (acc.)	lands (gen.)
women (gen.)	me (dat.)	you (gen.)
window (abl.)	sailors (dat.)	victories (abl.)
daughter (acc.)	we (nom.)	roads (dat.)
chance (abl.)	money (acc.)	life (abl.)
glories (acc.)	girls (dat.)	you (dat. pl.)

insula	
insulae	
	insulis
insulam	
	insulis

ego	
	nostri, nostrum
me	
	nobis

tu	
	vestri, vestrum
	vobis
te	

	aquae
	aquarum
aquam	
	aquis

Derivatives Crossword

Across

2. Hispania (8)
5. fuga (7)
6. via (7)
9. culpa (7)
13. insula (7)
14. terra (7)
17. fama (8)
22. gratia (9)
23. herba (9)
24. injuria (9)
25. nauta (8)
26. stella (7)

Down

1. gloria (7)
3. aqua (8)
4. victoria (10)
7. unda (8)
8. silva (6)
10. vita (7)
11. pecunia (9)
12. fortuna (9)
15. femina (8)
16. luna (5)
18. mora (10)
19. lingua (9)
20. ira (5)
21. memoria (8)

Grammar Crossword

Across

2. me (acc.) (2)
4. crowns (nom.) (7)
6. of me (3)
8. waves (acc.) (5)
9. of you (pl.) (7)
10. thanks (acc.) (7)
13. of the forest (6)
17. of the water (5)
18. you (pl. dat.) (5)
19. fights (abl.) (6)
20. the moon's (5)
22. money (acc.) (8)
24. flight (acc.) (5)
28. you (dat.) (4)
30. a bear's (5)
31. I (3)
32. hours (abl.) (5)
34. fault (dat.) (6)
35. country (nom.) (6)
36. the sailors' (8)
37. fame (dat.) (5)

Down

1. togas (acc.) (5)
2. memories (abl.) (8)
3. us (abl.) (5)
5. delays (acc.) (5)
7. dinner (nom.) (4)
11. eagles (dat.) (7)
12. a queen's (7)
14. of the islands (9)
15. life (abl.) (4)
16. fortune (abl.) (7)
21. of the roads (6)
23. window (acc.) (9)
24. daughter (dat.) (6)
25. dawn (acc.) (7)
26. girls' (9)
27. glories (acc.) (7)
29. Italy (acc.) (7)
32. plants (nom.) (6)
33. a star (acc.) (7)

TRANSFORMER

The idea of this game is to turn one Latin sentence into another, one word at a time. At each stage, one of the words of the original sentence becomes a blank. You are given three choices, but only one makes sense. Select the one that makes sense and write it in the blank. This word stays in the sentence from now on. At the end of the process, you have a new, completely transformed sentence.

For example:

Maria lunam videt. (Mary sees the moon.)

Stage 1: _____ lunam videt.   vita
                                                  ursas
                                                  femina

Vita does not fit because the meaning does not make sense.
Ursas does not fit because it is accusative plural.
Femina fits. Write it in the blank of this stage and the following stages.

Stage 2: __Femina__ _____ videt.   silvarum
                                                  filias
                                                  fugam

Silvarum does not fit because it is genitive plural.
Filias fits because it is accusative and the meaning makes sense.
Fugam is accusative but the meaning does not fit.

Stage 3: __Femina__ __filias__ _____   habet
                                                  sedet
                                                  vocant

Habet fits; it is 3rd person singular and the meaning makes sense.
Sedet does not fit because the meaning does not make sense.
Vocant does not make sense because it is plural.

Stage 4: __Femina__ __filias__ __habet__

The original sentence:
        Maria lunam videt. (Mary sees the moon.)

has been transformed into the new sentence:
        Femina filias habet. (The woman has daughters.)

18

TRANSFORMER

1. Femina togam portat. (The woman is carrying a toga.)

   Femina togam _____.

   _____ togam _____.

   _____ _____ _____.

   navigat
   videt
   ambulant

   lunam
   nauta
   herba

   iram
   memoriam
   insulam

2. Italia silvas habet. (Italy has forests.)

   Italia _____ habet.

   _____ _____ habet.

   _____ _____ _____.

   aquarum
   pecuniam
   ursae

   aquila
   regina
   fugae

   habitat
   portant
   amat

3. Puellae fenestram lavant. (The girls are washing the window.)

   _____ fenestram lavant.

   _____ _____ lavant.

   _____ _____ _____.

   injuria
   Maria
   filiae

   mensam
   culpam
   victoriam

   sedent
   movent
   clamant

PARSE STRINGS

fenestrarum	2nd person singular
videbitis	ablative singular
superant	genitive plural
injurias	dative singular
gratiis	1st person singular
timebat	ablative plural
paras	3rd person plural
morae	accusative singular
spectabamus	accusative plural
viam	2nd person plural
vita	3rd person singular
navigo	1st person plural

Match Up

nautical	victim
coronation	duck
lunar	star
constellation	king
culprit	rude
aquatic	masculine
vitality	ship
patrician	unlucky
gracious	energy
feminine	plebeian
victorious	eclipse
fortunate	conquered

LESSON 3

WORD SEARCH

```
M U R O C O L F R U M E N T U M Z H
O W T C K Z L S O L U P O P W I N E
S D T K X F R T G W I P Z V D L R Q
F I N D R G K K I N K V T U J D J U
O O I U V X P R N B J V L R G I V O
R T D D M Z A A C V T K T J K S M V
O R V T U B X Z L P Q T D R P C J O
R O W N R A J D O M I N U M Q I V T
U H Y A R X G P X R L S R J W P E A
M L B C C A M P O R U M I W N U R C
B K R Z M S L C K L Q B O L F L B C
Y K G U S O M E Y L T H S P U O O E
R L R W I I F N G V Z I C S P C H P
Z I V N C C L M E A G R I I R I O R
S K K R I O K N L N T G N L B J D R
R M Z Q M S T R A N R O X R X U Y A
W L D K A I O I R E P M I D R H M M
H H B R S R T H T T K M B E L L I S
```

friends (dat.)   forums (gen.)   walls (abl.)
years (nom.)   grain (acc.)   eyes (abl.)
barbarian (gen.)   joys (abl.)   towns (acc.)
wars (abl.)   garden (dat.)   sin (dat.)
fields (gen.)   command (abl.)   peoples (acc.)
food (acc.)   envoy (dat.)   signs (acc.)
student (abl.)   places (gen.)   allies (acc.)
master (acc.)   games (nom.)   backs (abl.)
horse (abl.)   world (abl.)   winds (abl.)
                                         word (abl.)

signum	
signi	signorum
signum	
	signis

gladius	gladii
	gladiorum
gladium	

hortus	
horti	
	hortis
horto	

	auxiliorum
	auxiliis
auxilium	

Derivatives Crossword

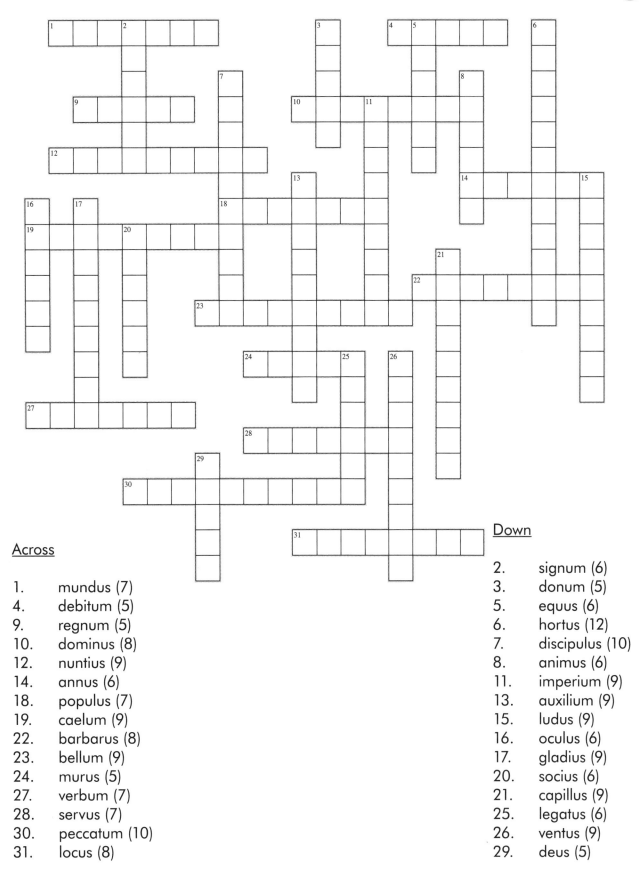

Across

1. mundus (7)
4. debitum (5)
9. regnum (5)
10. dominus (8)
12. nuntius (9)
14. annus (6)
18. populus (7)
19. caelum (9)
22. barbarus (8)
23. bellum (9)
24. murus (5)
27. verbum (7)
28. servus (7)
30. peccatum (10)
31. locus (8)

Down

2. signum (6)
3. donum (5)
5. equus (6)
6. hortus (12)
7. discipulus (10)
8. animus (6)
11. imperium (9)
13. auxilium (9)
15. ludus (9)
16. oculus (6)
17. gladius (9)
20. socius (6)
21. capillus (9)
25. legatus (6)
26. ventus (9)
29. deus (5)

Grammar Crossword

Across

2. words (nom.) (5)
4. kingdom (dat.) (5)
6. field (abl.) (5)
8. of the standards (8)
9. the people (acc.) (7)
10. of friends (8)
12. wines (abl.) (5)
17. of the wars (8)
18. lambs (nom.) (4)
19. gifts (acc.) (4)
22. games (acc.) (5)
25. lords (nom.) (6)
26. envoy (dat.) (6)
28. a weapon (acc.) (5)
29. gardens (dat.) (6)
31. aid (abl.) (7)
32. eyes (acc.) (6)
33. swords (abl.) (7)
34. the horse's (4)
35. a student's (9)
36. grain (abl.) (8)

Down

1. barbarians (acc.) (8)
2. winds (abl.) (6)
3. place (dat.) (4)
5. slaves (dat.) (6)
6. food (acc.) (5)
7. joys (nom.) (6)
11. towns (dat.) (7)
13. battle (abl.) (7)
14. the world (abl.) (5)
15. hairs (abl.) (8)
16. year (dat.) (4)
20. a forum (dat.) (4)
21. cloud (acc.) (6)
23. debts (acc.) (6)
24. of messages (9)
27. mind (nom.) (6)
28. backs (acc.) (5)
30. a son (acc.) (6)

TRANSFORMER

1. Populus auxilium dabit. (The people will give aid.)

   Populus _____ dabit.

    praemio
    signum
    pecunia

   Populus _____ _____ .

    portant
    navigat
    videbat

   _____ _____ _____ .

    legatos
    barbarus
    servum

2. Dominus equos spectabat. (The master was looking at the horses.)

   _____ equos spectabat.

    amicos
    legatum
    filius

   _____ _____ spectabat.

    ventum
    hortum
    campis

   _____ _____ _____ .

    parabit
    navigabat
    ambulabant

3. Oppida aquam habent. (The towns have water.)

   _____ aquam habent.

    ecclesias
    gaudium
    equi

   _____ aquam _____ .

    pugnant
    vident
    portamus

   _____ _____ _____ .

    cibus
    gratias
    agnos

Match Up

gladiator	primary
auxiliary	fan
barbaric	peaceful
discipline	subordinate
design	arena
verbose	fashion
belligerent	silly
delegate	wordy
annual	training
ventilation	civilized
ludicrous	convention
dominant	yearly

LESSON 4

WORD SEARCH

```
X K G C P R T F S B X T R L P A X L
K W L A K Y Z S S I L E Y L E R S Z
R N L N N X D U I L T Y R L L I Y S
I L P I Q O J I R S V S L N N T U C
F G K S L X N R O N E I O I H T V O
O R N O L O J A P A M P M H R L E R
K I R I C R W U M V Z O T I P S R P
C I P T S T D Q E I H H V E Z I I O
S I I R N F Q A T S I C U L M R T R
I S V Y O U L S I T I P A C V T A I
B L K I I C N U K L K T T N J A S S
R J K N T O S H M M E C E D X R J S
U M Q K M A M I L I T I S L T F U P
V U U E C W T D K R N R M A T R I S
E M N T T W R I E Q P I K T U R Y Z
D S I T N O P T S G Q T S A T P Q K
F G Q T V E A H J N D P T W K K H R
K W L H H P C W R M Q U A T T U O R
```

aquarius	enemy (nom.)	bridge (gen.)
dog (gen.)	fire (gen.)	four
head (gen.)	light (gen.)	five
hundred	mother (gen.)	king (nom.)
state (gen.)	soldier (gen.)	scorpio
body (gen.)	thousand	seven
ten	ship (nom.)	taurus
sorrow (gen.)	night (gen.)	time (gen.)
river (gen.)	name (nom.)	city (gen.)
brother (gen.)	father (nom.)	truth (nom.)
man (gen.)	peace (nom.)	courage (nom.)

Derivatives Crossword

Across

1. mons (5)
6. pons (7)
7. urbs (6)
9. pars (8)
13. tres (8)
14. corpus (11)
16. soror (8)
19. mater (9)
21. unus (6)

22. nox (7)
24. pater (9)
26. lex (5)
27. caput (7)
29. centum (7)
30. crux (7)
31. frater (10)

Down

2. tempus (7)
3. nomen (4)
4. hostis (9)
5. mors (9)
8. ignis (7)
10. canis (6)
11. miles (8)
12. dolor (8)
15. ordo (6)

17. imperator (10)
18. virtus (6)
19. mille (7)
20. navis (5)
23. pax (7)
25. homo (8)
28. lux (5)

Grammar Crossword

Across

1. of the state (9)
8. of sorrow (7)
9. of the cross (6)
11. the centurion's (11)
13. five (7)
14. of the hill (6)
17. of night (6)
21. a father's (6)
22. of the body (8)
25. a man's (7)
27. the sister's (7)
28. of law (5)
29. the ship's (5)
32. a commander's (11)
34. of the head (7)
35. of a bridge (6)

Down

2. of time (8)
3. the voice's (5)
4. of the name (7)
5. of the city (5)
6. virtue's (8)
7. of the river (8)
10. Caesar's (8)
12. of an enemy (6)
15. of truth (9)
16. of light (5)
18. a dog's (5)
19. the king's (5)
20. the brother's (7)
23. of rank (7)
24. a soldier's (7)
26. of the mountain (6)
30. of a part (6)
31. thousand (5)
33. of peace (5)

TRANSFORMER

1. Miles tela portat. (The soldier is carrying weapons.)

Miles _____ portat.

Miles _____ _____ .

_____ _____ _____ .

frumentum
gladiorum
frater

vides
habebunt
lavabat

Italia
centurio
patri

2. Caesar gladium habet. (Caesar has a sword.)

_____ gladium habet.

_____ _____ habet.

_____ _____ _____ .

militis
rex
viros

regnum
oculis
canis

superant
monebo
occupabit

3. Regina equos amat. (The queen loves horses.)

Regina equos _____ .

_____ equos _____ .

_____ _____ _____ .

ambulat
vident
timet

canis
patris
agnos

aquae
ursam
luna

PARSE STRINGS

capillis	1st person plural present
regna	accusative singular
urbis	3rd person singular future
jubebit	ablative plural
liberabam	number
gladio	3rd person plural future
nox	accusative plural
pugnamus	2nd person plural present
dabunt	1st person plural future
murum	genitive singular
habebimus	nominative singular
decem	2nd person singular imperfect
verborum	genitive plural
timebas	1st person singular imperfect
movetis	ablative singular

Match Up

temporary	confused
pacific	civilian
military	violent
urban	army
corps	permanent
igneous	fahrenheit
nocturnal	rural
partition	volcanic
lucid	wipe out
dolorous	vampire
decimate	cheerful
centigrade	union

LESSON 5

WORD SEARCH

```
Z M M K J V R C B B T Z Y T H H P T
P S U X L D A V Y D W S G T N P D N
R E L Q N Q C T M R E N T L P Y Z M
I M T Y N W M A C C K U M R H N M U
M P O C R W T A U N C T K K J N M T
O E F N F O D N L I A L O N G I K L
S R X M T N D O S I N S N C R B N A
W C N U A V M N N S O O I T R E T
S O L O R R M H N Z T K V M X R M X
H R T U A A T K Q W D S N O R U K V
A G M P G C P R L A A H B L R Y I M
R G R N M G R R C E M K C A W U M B
T T O V A A F R P E G I N H T Y M D
N S M F T F U E M R R O X F J M U T
O M L T U F P Q P H B T Z O N C S M
C R M H T J L J M R K C A B R K K Z
W A E T E R N I S U Q M W K G P K X
R T P Q R N R Z S A N E L P M W T R
```

eternal (n. abl. pl.)

high (n. acc. sing.)

good (f. gen. pl.)

sure (f. abl. sing.)

against

long (n. gen. sing.)

great (m. acc. pl.)

bad (f. dat. pl.)

much (m. abl. sing.)

new (m. gen. pl.)

never

now

small (m. dat. sing.)

full (f. acc. pl.)

first (m. acc. pl.)

next (f. abl. sing.)

often

holy (n. acc. pl.)

second (f. gen. pl.)

always

as

only (n. abl. sing.)

highest (n. gen. sing.)

third (m. dat. sing.)

all (f. acc. sing.)

safe (f. acc. sing)

malum	
	malorum
malum	
	malis

longa	
	longarum
	longis
longa	

mea	
meae	
	meis
	meis

novus	
novo	novis
	novis

Derivatives Crossword

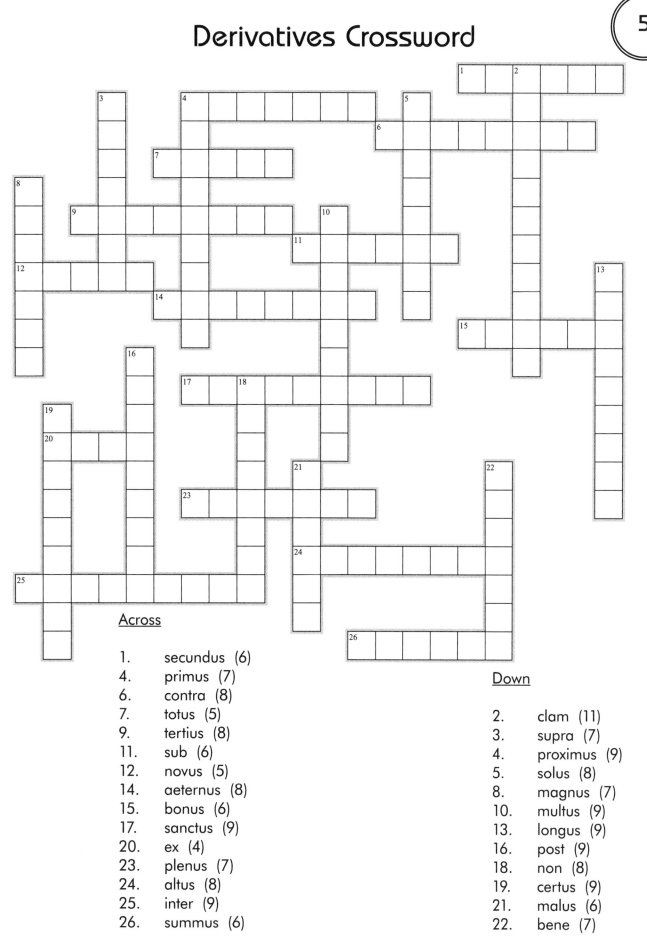

Across

1. secundus (6)
4. primus (7)
6. contra (8)
7. totus (5)
9. tertius (8)
11. sub (6)
12. novus (5)
14. aeternus (8)
15. bonus (6)
17. sanctus (9)
20. ex (4)
23. plenus (7)
24. altus (8)
25. inter (9)
26. summus (6)

Down

2. clam (11)
3. supra (7)
4. proximus (9)
5. solus (8)
8. magnus (7)
10. multus (9)
13. longus (9)
16. post (9)
18. non (8)
19. certus (9)
21. malus (6)
22. bene (7)

Grammar Crossword

Across

5. not (3)
6. second (n. acc. sing.) (8)
8. under (3)
9. my (f. dat. sing.) (4)
10. next (f. nom. sing.) (7)
14. good (n. gen. pl.) (7)
16. out of (2)
17. after (4)
19. above (5)
20. often (5)
22. safe (m. acc. pl.) (5)
23. and (2)
24. your (n. abl. pl.) (4)
25. as (5)
26. first (f. acc. pl.) (6)
28. everlasting (f. gen. pl.) (10)
29. never (7)
31. between (5)
32. holy (f. nom. pl.) (7)
33. well (4)

Down

1. before (4)
2. against (6)
3. long (m. abl. sing.) (5)
4. always (6)
6. highest (f. abl. sing.) (5)
7. secretly (4)
8. only (n. dat. pl.) (5)
9. bad (f. abl. pl.) (5)
10. small (f. gen. sing.) (6)
11. new (f. acc. pl.) (5)
12. third (n. nom. sing.) (7)
13. sure (m. dat. pl.) (6)
15. many (f. acc. pl.) (6)
18. whole (m. gen. pl.) (7)
21. full (m. acc. sing.) (6)
27. great (n. acc. pl.) (5)
29. now (4)
30. high (f. dat. sing.) (5)

PARSE STRINGS

sanctas	preposition
tuis	genitive plural neuter
magni	accusative plural masculine
prima	ablative singular masculine
solus	adverb
saepe	genitive singular neuter
summo	accusative plural feminine
et	nominative plural feminine
meam	nominative singular masculine
tertiae	accusative singular neuter
plenorum	conjunction
longum	genitive plural feminine
post	dative plural masculine
proximos	accusative singular feminine
altarum	nominative singular feminine

Match Up

proximity	safe
beneficial	social
longitude	distance
novel	lack
interfere	unusual
sanctuary	airplane
plenty	part
altimeter	helpful
solitary	meddle
totality	latitude

Lesson 6

WORD SEARCH

```
K   P   Q   S   C   C   R   S   P   H
G   B   O   I   J   M   J   I   J   M
G   R   K   R   A   F   F   I   V   N
F   Z   Q   B   T   A   Y   C   I   W
Q   L   U   M   B   A   M   N   L   X
B   T   M   U   D   N   S   I   L   X
C   R   L   C   H   D   T   V   A   N
L   A   T   J   C   C   Y   O   R   D
L   U   C   I   A   E   P   R   U   C
N   M   A   L   L   E   S   P   M   Q
```

story (abl.)

Lucy (dat.)

gates (acc.)

provinces (dat.)

chair (acc.)

trumpet (acc.)

shadows (abl.)

farmhouses (gen.)

Lesson 7
WORD SEARCH

```
T S A U N A J C L X C N
L S H C A S A S C N A P
M I M K V C T L Q T Y M
U L K E T T Q K U R U E
R O C A A B G R C R K A
A C Q I H N A V A H T L
L I X T T M I R N M A U
L R N N Y H A L A C B T
E G C E D Y A T U Q E S
B A K I T M E R T C R I
A T Z C K O V Z I W N P
T G L S P Y X T M S A E
```

farmers (abl.)   doors (acc.)

altars (gen.)   nature (acc.)

cottages (acc.)   poet (acc.)

harps (abl.)   knowledge (dat.)

kitchen (dat.)   tablets (gen.)

letters (nom.)   shop (abl.)

fabula	
	fabularum
fabula	fabulis

	tabellae
tabellae	
	tabellas
	tabellis

agricola	
	agricolas
agricola	

sella	
	sellarum
	sellis
sellam	

Derivatives Crossword

Across

4. casa (6)
7. agricola (11)
8. culina (8)
10. epistula (7)
12. poeta (6)
16. scientia (10)
18. taberna (6)
19. scientia (7)
20. porta (5)
21. cithara (6)

Down

1. janua (7)
2. taberna (10)
3. villa (7)
5. natura (7)
6. culina (4)
9. scientia (10)
11. fabula (8)
13. villa (7)
14. janua (7)
15. umbra (8)
17. tuba (4)

Grammar Crossword

Across

2. cottage (dir. obj.) (5)
6. the guitar (dir. obj.) (8)
8. of nature (7)
9. gates (dir. obj.) (6)
10. (by) letters (9)
12. the gate's (6)
15. trumpet (dir. obj.) (5)
17. of shadows (8)
20. (in) stories (7)
21. for the provinces (10)
22. a chair (subject) (5)
26. knowledge (dir. obj.) (9)
28. poet (ind. obj.) (6)
29. tablets (dir. obj.) (8)
30. (in) cottages (5)
32. (by) knowledge (8)
34. farmhouses (dir. obj.) (6)
35. a shop's (8)
36. a letter (ind. obj.) (9)

Down

1. (with) Lucy (5)
2. (with) harps (8)
3. of the altars (6)
4. (with) poets (6)
5. (on) the altar (3)
7. a farmer (dir. obj.) (9)
11. (in) shops (8)
13. (in) the shadows (6)
14. trumpets (dir. obj.) (5)
15. (on) tablets (8)
16. nature (dir. obj.) (7)
18. doors (subject) (6)
19. farmhouse (ind. obj.) (6)
23. (with) farmers (9)
24. (in) chairs (6)
25. of stories (9)
27. kitchens (subject) (7)
31. doors (dir. obj.) (6)
33. (in) the kitchen (6)

Match Up

umbrella	hero
culinary	parasol
villain	careless
tavern	legendary
provincial	chef
guitar	gateway
natural	worldly
tube	string
fabled	inn
agriculture	pipe
conscientious	hunting
portal	artificial

Lesson 8
WORD SEARCH

```
M M L D D D N X W S M
W U R Y K R V L O U R
L M P J K I N C R N O
G R X U C C R O T A M
N A K I L A R S M I A
D Q L X M B M I J T N
V N N L I X J R L S O
M G N L I C L G R I S
X Q X L Q S P A D R T
P M A G I S T R O H C
L O L O T S O P A C Q
```

fields (dat.)	wolf (acc.)
apostle (abl.)	teacher (abl.)
Christian (nom.)	Mark (dat.)
Gauls (abl.)	Romans (acc.)
books (gen.)	village (gen.)

Lesson 9
WORD SEARCH

```
A  S  N  S  R  Y  N  J  V  R  Z  L
L  L  A  L  I  V  Y  K  W  L  Z  N
U  M  E  E  H  L  L  Z  W  K  M  X
C  K  V  V  C  W  E  L  G  A  M  M
I  T  A  T  D  U  B  G  N  M  U  X
R  H  N  Y  V  Z  L  D  N  R  W  O
E  N  G  V  K  G  A  O  O  A  T  I
P  K  E  M  W  T  V  R  R  U  V  R
G  R  L  D  I  C  I  J  C  U  N  E
F  Q  I  S  D  V  R  S  T  D  M  U
M  X  U  O  I  P  I  C  N  I  R  P
B  R  M  S  T  U  D  I  I  P  X  P
```

angels (dat.)	boy (gen.)
Gospel (acc.)	ages (gen.)
commands (abl.)	shield (abl.)
dangers (acc.)	zeal (gen.)
beginning (abl.)	men (gen.)

principii	
	principiis
principium	
	principiis

vici	vicorum
vico	vicis

studio	studiis
studio	studiis

libri	librorum
	libris
librum	

Derivatives Crossword

Across

2. puer (7)
4. studium (7)
7. principium (9)
8. angelus (7)
11. evangelium (10)
14. principium (9)
15. evangelium (11)
17. liber (7)
18. mandatum (7)
19. magister (7)
21. ager (11)
22. vicus (8)

Down

1. studium (6)
3. scutum (10)
5. saeculum (7)
6. mandatum (9)
9. periculum (5)
10. magister (10)
12. vir (11)
13. vir (6)
16. vir (7)
20. studium (5)

8-9

Grammar Crossword

Across

3. a teacher (subject) (8)
4. the book's (5)
5. the Gauls (dir. obj.) (6)
8. of the beginning (9)
9. Mark's (5)
10. enthusiasm (subject) (7)
12. (with) a Roman (6)
14. a shield (dir. obj.) (6)
15. men (subject) (4)
16. Mark (ind. obj.) (5)
18. boys (dir. obj.) (6)
19. a wolf (dir. obj.) (5)
22. the Gospels (dir. obj.) (9)
23. commands (subject) (7)
25. of the men (7)
28. a boy's (5)
29. (with) zeal (6)
30. of books (8)
31. a Christian's (10)
33. of the apostles (11)
35. wolves (subject) (4)
36. (in) the age (7)
37. dangers (dir. obj.) (8)
38. (from) Christians (11)

Down

1. the Gauls (ind. obj.) (6)
2. villages (subject) (4)
3. a teacher (dir. obj.) (9)
6. (out of) the village (4)
7. an apostle (dir. obj.) (9)
11. of the Gospel (9)
13. (from) the field (4)
17. of angels (9)
18. beginnings (subject) (9)
20. (by) commands (8)
21. ages (ind. obj.) (8)
24. fields (dir. obj.) (5)
26. the Romans' (9)
27. (in) danger (8)
32. an angel (dir. obj.) (7)
34. (with) shields (6)

54

libro	nominative singular neuter
januarum	accusative plural feminine
scutum	accusative singular masculine
provinciis	nominative singular masculine
mandata	genitive plural masculine
puerorum	genitive plural feminine
citharas	nominative plural masculine
scientiae	ablative plural feminine
agricolam	accusative singular feminine
ager	ablative singular masculine
magistri	nominative plural neuter
viros	genitive singular feminine
tabellam	accusative plural masculine

Match Up

vicinity	judge
secular	diligent
magistrate	layman
principal	dangerous
studious	missionary
Gallic	preacher
mandate	secondary
evangelist	order
apostle	strong
perilous	immature
virile	neighborhood
puerile	French

Derivatives Crossword

Across

1.   come together and touch (7)
3.   live in (7)
6.   harmony (7)
7.   bring from one place to another (7)
11. physical or emotional well-being (7)
13. not present (6)
14. musical instruments played by beating (10)
16. continuous and eternal (9)
18. send from one place to another (8)
19. completely ruin (7)
21. change to match or move with (6)
22. preserving wildlife and natural habitat (12)
26. order (7)
27. make aware (6)
28. convert from one language to another (9)
29. go off the path (7)
34. point of view (11)
39. turn over (6)
40. of equal parts of 100 (7)
43. trust (10)
44. draw liquid from (6)
45. false or erroneous belief (8)
46. win over to one's point of view (8)

Down

2.   linear accumulation of numbers (8)
4.   exciting, slightly dangerous experience (9)
5.   tool (10)
8.   bring a child into a family (5)
9.   put together to see similarities (7)
10. pardon a sin (7)
12. move a plant from one bed to another (10)
13. opposite of relative (8)
15. give an image or idea of (8)
17. determining situation (12)
18. carry something across a region (9)
20. not concrete (8)
23. misusing to cause injury (7)
24. put into (6)
25. without defect (7)
26. sail around (14)
29. push down (7)
30. rely on for support (6)
31. convert into writing (10)
32. opposite of abstract (8)
33. draw a line around (12)
35. teach (8)
36. exchange thoughts or ideas (11)
37. find a way around (10)
38. write music (7)
41. put together (7)
42. aggressive opposition (8)

Grammar Crossword

Across

3.   it was (4)
4.   sine __(zeal)__ (6)
5.   per __(the shadows)__ (6)
8.   de __(knowledge)__ (8)
10.   you will be (4)
12.   e __(danger)__ (8)
13.   we were (6)
16.   I will be (3)
17.   cum __(Lucy)__ (5)
18.   he is (3)
19.   they are (4)
21.   circum __(the village)__ (5)
24.   trans __(the altar)__ (4)
27.   we are (5)
31.   ad __(the farmers)__ (9)
33.   trans __(the province)__ (10)
34.   de __(books)__ (6)
36.   ad __(a man)__ (5)
37.   cum __(the boys)__ (6)
38.   you (pl.) were (6)

Down

1.   per __(the field)__ (5)
2.   you were (4)
4.   trans __(the ages)__ (7)
6.   cum __(angels)__ (7)
7.   per __(the door)__ (6)
9.   ad __(the farmhouses)__ (6)
10.   they will be (5)
11.   per __(the age)__ (8)
13.   she will be (4)
14.   de __(letters)__ (9)
15.   cum __(poets)__ (6)
20.   sine __(stories)__ (7)
22.   a __(Mark)__ (5)
23.   de __(the chair)__ (5)
25.   I was (4)
26.   in __(the beginning)__ (9)
28.   sine __(a teacher)__ (8)
29.   you (pl.) will be (6)
30.   circum __(the shields)__ (5)
32.   ad __(the Gauls)__ (6)
35.   cum __(a wolf)__ (4)

Lesson 12
WORD SEARCH

```
T   T   L   P   Q   E   M   E   Z   C   S
N   R   L   T   R   P   R   K   N   F   U
U   L   H   R   A   A   R   T   A   B   M
B   N   A   T   V   B   N   G   T   L   A
A   S   B   R   E   T   A   L   A   T   B
T   L   E   K   X   M   G   D   B   M   A
U   S   N   D   T   Q   P   L   I   Q   C
L   L   H   Z   M   P   V   T   T   Y   O
A   A   R   A   B   O   J   H   A   J   V
S   S   I   T   A   B   A   T   S   N   G
E   X   S   P   E   C   T   A   B   A   T
```

I will plow	they will greet
she was giving	to keep
you err	you (pl.) were standing
he was waiting for	they tempt
she will swim	we were calling

Lesson 13
WORD SEARCH

```
R  F  L  E  B  I  M  U  S  M  C  Z
R  O  B  E  D  N  O  P  S  E  R  R
R  T  V  A  L  E  R  E  N  F  I  P
L  I  Z  T  U  N  Y  M  L  D  F  D
K  B  K  H  K  G  C  W  E  T  M  K
Z  E  C  C  T  R  E  B  R  A  Z  M
L  N  H  A  E  V  A  B  B  L  A  L
K  E  Z  V  N  T  M  E  U  N  Z  N
K  T  M  E  O  L  C  F  E  N  H  J
X  T  R  N  M  A  P  B  T  B  T  T
L  Y  Z  T  L  T  A  N  V  M  M  F
W  M  D  P  W  S  W  R  K  M  M  R
```

they will increase	I was pleasing
they beware of	I will answer
we will weep	she was laughing
you were staying	he will hold
it warns	to be well

tenebam	
	tenebant

	augebimus
augebis	

	stamus
	statis

eram	
erat	

das	
dat	

Derivatives Crossword

Across

4. placeo (8)
7. aro (6)
8. augeo (7)
9. sto (6)
10. tempto (10)
15. rideo (10)
17. teneo (9)
19. moneo (8)
21. maneo (7)
22. voco (5)
23. erro (7)
24. do (5)
25. erro (10)

Down

1. fleo (6)
2. valeo (8)
3. exspecto (11)
4. placeo (6)
5. sto (7)
6. teneo (6)
11. moneo (7)
12. respondeo (7)
13. servo (8)
14. voco (10)
16. caveo (7)
18. saluto (10)
20. do (8)

Grammar Crossword

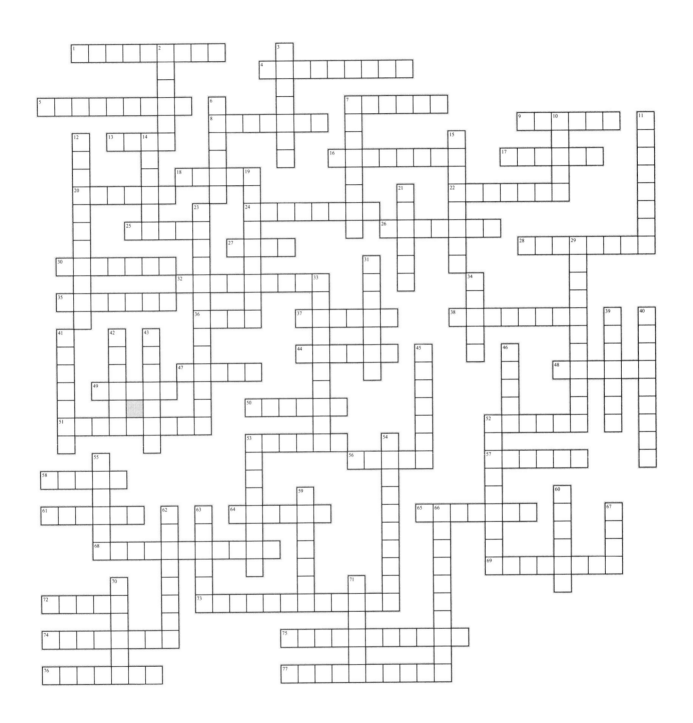

Across

1. you (pl.) were well (9)
4. you (pl.) will swim (9)
5. I reply (9)
7. to warn (6)
8. it was increasing (7)
9. it pleases (6)
13. to give (4)
16. to tempt (8)
17. to err (6)
18. it warns (5)
20. I please (6)
22. she was calling (7)
24. they will remain (8)
25. to stand (5)
26. you will err (7)
27. it is standing (4)
28. they will be well (8)
30. you tempt (7)
32. we will call (9)
35. we are laughing (7)
36. they give (4)
37. we are weeping (6)
38. to greet (8)
44. it was standing (6)
47. he is well (5)
48. to be well (6)
49. she guards against (5)
50. she was weeping (6)
51. we will increase (9)
52. you will stand (6)
53. I greet (6)
56. to weep (5)
57. to laugh (6)
58. you were giving (5)
61. I will increase (6)
64. to remain (6)
65. you were holding (7)
68. he will wait for (11)
69. they were holding (8)
72. to plow (5)
73. they were waiting for (12)
74. you were pleasing (8)
75. you were waiting for (11)
76. to please (7)
77. to reply (10)

Down

2. to increase (6)
3. I was swimming (7)
6. they will give (6)
7. they will warn (8)
10. they plow (5)
11. it will please (8)
12. you will reply (11)
14. they laugh (6)
15. I was keeping (8)
19. it was tempting (9)
21. I will err (6)
23. you (pl.) were replying (13)
29. you (pl.) are waiting for (11)
31. she is greeting (7)
33. they were greeting (10)
34. I will plow (5)
39. I was warning (7)
40. we will hold (9)
41. I was remaining (7)
42. to call (6)
43. he will laugh (7)
45. to keep (7)
46. it remains (5)
52. they will keep (9)
53. you will keep (8)
54. they will tempt (10)
55. to beware of (6)
59. it was erring (7)
60. I will warn (6)
62. we were weeping (8)
63. to swim (6)
66. to wait for (10)
67. it plows (4)
70. to hold (6)
71. I will beware of (6)

TRANSFORMER

1. Agricolae in villa manebunt. (The farmers will stay in the farmhouse.)

   Agricolae in villa _____.

   natant
   laborant
   erat

   Agricolae in _____ _____.

   campum
   villarum
   agris

   _____ in _____ _____.

   viri
   libri
   lupos

2. Canis circum casam ambulabat. (A dog was walking around the cottage.)

   Canis circum _____ ambulabat.

   tabella
   naturam
   insulam

   _____ circum _____ ambulabat.

   nauta
   pueri
   tuba

   _____ circum _____ _____.

   errant
   spectabat
   navigabat

3. Imperator mandatum exspectabat. (The general was waiting for the command.)

   Imperator _____ exspectabat.

   filiis
   nuntium
   portam

   Imperator _____ _____.

   timebant
   vides
   cavebat

   _____ _____ _____.

   pueros
   hortus
   populus

PARSE STRINGS

temptabam	3rd person plural present
vales	infinitive
ridebimus	3rd person singular future
errabunt	3rd person singular imperfect
ero	1st person singular present
stabat	3rd person plural imperfect
natabamus	2nd person singular present
flet	2nd person plural imperfect
dare	3rd person plural future
augent	1st person plural imperfect
cavebit	1st person plural present
tenebatis	1st person singular future
sum	1st person singular imperfect
manemus	3rd person singular present
exspectabant	1st person plural future

Match Up

ridicule	charity
augment	false
mansion	waste
erroneous	praise
conserve	warn
tempting	silent
valuable	cheap
donor	fertile
vocal	disgusting
caution	agitated
arable	bungalow
placid	expand

Lesson 14
WORD SEARCH

O	F	S	R	M	T	R	V	S	Q	K	D
D	R	U	E	T	T	G	I	M	M	F	E
E	N	M	G	H	N	T	N	B	Q	R	Y
R	Z	I	I	J	I	U	M	K	E	P	Z
C	L	G	T	V	W	P	D	R	M	P	H
B	M	A	I	X	O	J	R	A	W	J	N
L	I	V	S	N	K	U	D	U	C	I	S
H	C	B	I	N	C	L	N	R	C	Y	X
D	P	T	I	N	M	X	K	Q	J	H	F
L	X	B	R	T	D	K	L	V	L	Q	N
M	C	N	T	S	U	M	I	D	A	R	T
V	K	F	N	M	K	M	P	K	Q	P	Y

we do

he is drinking

they are falling

I believe

to run

you are leading

she is putting

you rule

we hand over

you (pl.) are living

Lesson 15
WORD SEARCH

```
J  M  S  B  D  C  L  M  X  T  T
S  T  D  C  K  H  I  Q  N  P  T
A  X  T  T  R  T  G  A  G  A  D
B  J  N  O  T  I  B  R  B  L  I
E  C  V  I  L  E  B  E  R  T  C
D  A  T  H  T  L  D  U  I  X  E
N  N  W  E  R  U  U  C  N  R  B
E  E  P  W  A  N  N  N  M  T  A
F  R  K  L  T  I  N  D  T  R  M
E  E  C  D  V  D  V  M  J  R  B
D  E  D  I  M  U  S  T  C  T  J
```

to sing	she sends
he was closing	they were seeking
you were defending	they are writing
I was saying	they raise up
we are eating	it conquers

	mittebamus
	mittebatis

vivo	
	vivunt

	regitis
regit	

agebam	agebamus

pono	
ponit	

Derivatives Crossword

14-15

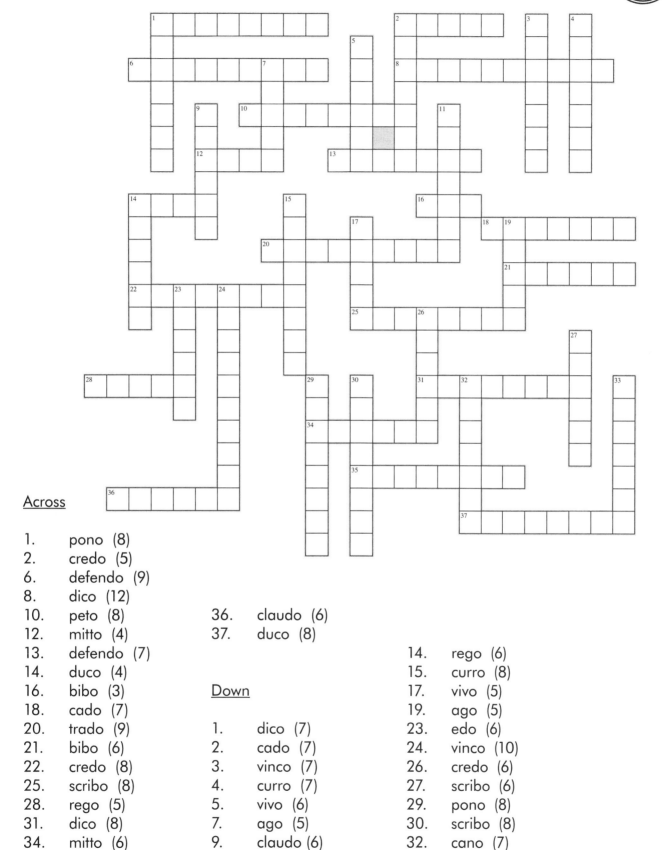

Across

1. pono (8)
2. credo (5)
6. defendo (9)
8. dico (12)
10. peto (8)
12. mitto (4)
13. defendo (7)
14. duco (4)
16. bibo (3)
18. cado (7)
20. trado (9)
21. bibo (6)
22. credo (8)
25. scribo (8)
28. rego (5)
31. dico (8)
34. mitto (6)
35. bibo (8)
36. claudo (6)
37. duco (8)

Down

1. dico (7)
2. cado (7)
3. vinco (7)
4. curro (7)
5. vivo (6)
7. ago (5)
9. claudo (6)
11. mitto (7)

14. rego (6)
15. curro (8)
17. vivo (5)
19. ago (5)
23. edo (6)
24. vinco (10)
26. credo (6)
27. scribo (6)
29. pono (8)
30. scribo (8)
32. cano (7)
33. duco (7)

75

Grammar Crossword

Across

4. you are leading (5)
6. we were conquering (10)
9. we were closing (11)
12. they were living (8)
14. you are raising up (6)
21. they were conquering (9)
22. he is closing (7)
23. they rule (6)
24. I seek (4)
25. I was writing (9)
28. to defend (9)
29. they are handing over (7)
31. I run (5)
32. I was leading (7)
33. I was living (7)
35. she was sending (8)
37. to hand over (7)
38. they were running (9)
40. it rules (5)
41. to rule (6)
43. to conquer (7)
45. she is defending (8)
49. they seek (6)
50. to believe (7)
51. you do (4)
52. you were ruling (7)
54. she was drinking (7)
55. I fall (4)
56. I was putting (7)
60. I am writing (6)
62. you conquer (6)
63. we are running (8)
65. they drink (6)
66. they were leading (8)
69. you (pl.) were drinking (9)
70. to place (6)
71. to say (6)
72. to eat (5)
73. you were handing over (8)
74. she is seeking (5)

Down

1. you are living (5)
2. it sends (6)
3. we defend (10)
5. they believe (7)
7. they send (7)
8. they were raising up (9)
10. he is singing (5)
11. she is putting (5)
13. to seek (6)
15. they are writing (8)
16. I hand over (5)
17. to raise up (7)
18. you (pl.) were defending (12)
19. to close (8)
20. to run (7)
22. it falls (5)
26. she was singing (7)
27. to lead (6)
30. to fall (6)
31. we close (9)
34. I was saying (7)
36. we are falling (7)
39. I eat (3)
42. you were eating (6)
43. to live (6)
44. we were believing (10)
46. to act (5)
47. to write (8)
48. to sing (6)
49. we put (7)
53. they are eating (5)
57. they are acting (5)
58. you were saying (7)
59. they say (6)
61. he was believing (8)
64. to send (7)
65. to drink (6)
67. I sing (4)
68. he was acting (6)

TRANSFORMER

1. Marcus trans viam ambulat. (Mark is walking across the road.)

   Marcus trans viam _____ .   dabat
                                                          currit
                                                          natat

   Marcus trans _____ _____.   ager
                                                          equos
                                                          vicum

   Marcus _____ _____ _____.   ad
                                                          cum
                                                          sine

   _____ _____ _____ _____.   Mariae
                                                          Romani
                                                          puer

2. Poeta bellorum fabulam canit. (The poet is singing a story of wars.)
   (A genitive phrase consists of two nouns, one of which is in the genitive case, such as
   bellorum fabulam = "a story of wars".)

   Poeta _____ fabulam canit.   culinis
                                                          memorias
                                                          proelii

   Poeta _____ fabulam _____.   dicunt
                                                          currit
                                                          scribit

   _____ _____ fabulam _____.   filias
                                                          imperator
                                                          signum

   _____ _____ _____ _____.   famam
                                                          epistularum
                                                          tela

Parse Strings

mittebatis	3rd person singular imperfect
currimus	1st person singular present
vivunt	3rd person singular present
tollo	3rd person plural present
edebant	1st person plural imperfect
credebam	infinitive
scribis	2nd person plural present
dicebat	2nd person plural imperfect
bibebamus	3rd person plural imperfect
regit	2nd person singular imperfect
canere	2nd person singular present
defendebas	1st person plural present
clauditis	1st person singular imperfect

Match Up

credulous	pale
positive	winner
inedible	waterfall
vivid	guzzle
conduct	delicious
victor	broadcast
current	gullible
transmit	former
predict	negative
cascade	foretell
imbibe	behavior

Lesson 16
WORD SEARCH

```
L  S  I  T  I  N  U  P  R  O  L
S  N  Z  V  G  M  N  F  I  H  T
C  M  F  G  R  T  P  T  M  N  R
I  S  T  B  X  R  N  E  U  V  F
T  U  K  S  T  E  L  I  D  I  D
X  M  R  U  S  K  M  M  N  I  V
K  I  S  M  W  R  H  I  K  M  T
N  R  D  I  O  K  R  N  D  G  G
H  E  N  D  N  E  M  U  N  I  S
W  P  N  U  M  E  L  H  T  K  T
M  A  H  A  B  B  V  D  X  B  Z
```

we are opening	you are fortifying
we hear	you (pl.) do punish
they are sleeping	he knows
to finish	I feel
it hinders	you come

Lesson 17
WORD SEARCH

J	N	J	K	Y	P	D	L
R	W	I	B	U	N	E	P
M	U	Q	T	Q	L	S	S
E	X	C	U	I	X	A	Q
I	Z	I	H	O	R	N	U
D	D	I	G	C	D	D	I
O	N	P	G	Z	X	B	S
H	N	Z	Y	H	E	R	I

tomorrow	what?
why?	who?
yesterday	because
today	but
nothing	where?

82

puniebas	
	puniebant

	aperimus
	aperiunt

scio	scimus

sentiebas	
sentiebat	

finis	
	finiunt

Derivatives Crossword

Across

4. scio (10)
6. sentio (9)
8. dormio (7)
11. scio (9)
12. dormio (9)
15. scio (7)
17. finio (5)
18. sentio (9)
19. venio (9)

Down

1. audio (7)
2. audio (8)
3. impedio (10)
5. venio (5)
7. munio (10)
9. punio (8)
10. audio (8)
13. finio (6)
14. aperio (8)
16. sentio (6)

Grammar Crossword

Across

4. we were hearing (10)
8. they were punishing (9)
9. to punish (6)
10. because (4)
12. why? (3)
13. we were opening (11)
15. tomorrow (4)
17. I am fortifying (5)
20. to hear (6)
23. to hinder (8)
25. yesterday (4)
26. but (3)
29. what? (4)
31. we feel (8)
32. they were fortifying (9)
34. they finish (7)
36. nothing (5)
37. to come (6)
42. I come (5)
45. they know (6)
46. they were sleeping (10)
47. to open (7)
48. they feel (8)
49. she comes (5)
50. we are hindering (9)

Down

1. I was sleeping (9)
2. you were hearing (8)
3. we punish (7)
5. to finish (6)
6. I was opening (9)
7. they hear (7)
11. she knows (4)
14. to fortify (6)
16. you (pl.) knew (9)
18. who? (4)
19. you open (6)
21. we are sleeping (8)
22. you (pl.) are finishing (7)
24. we come (7)
25. today (5)
27. to feel (7)
28. we were hindering (12)
30. where? (3)
33. you were punishing (8)
35. he was hindering (10)
38. he feels (6)
39. I was finishing (8)
40. it hears (5)
41. to sleep (7)
43. to know (5)
44. you are fortifying (5)

Match Up

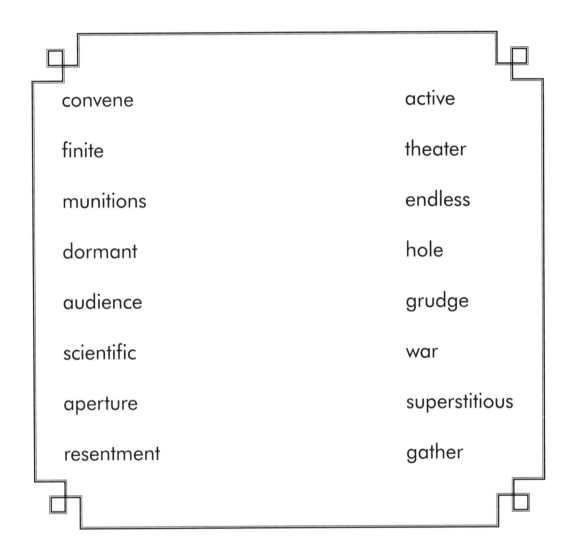

convene   active

finite   theater

munitions   endless

dormant   hole

audience   grudge

scientific   war

aperture   superstitious

resentment   gather

Lesson 18
WORD SEARCH

```
K  I  Z  E  R  F  M  Q  R  T  J  P
M  Z  N  R  M  F  M  J  C  I  T  I
E  R  T  O  J  O  W  T  T  M  V  S
N  Q  N  M  I  Y  R  M  L  O  B  C
I  Z  C  A  H  T  U  E  L  R  Z  A
G  K  W  L  D  R  C  U  S  I  F  T
R  L  H  C  O  J  N  E  L  B  W  O
I  X  V  T  R  T  J  T  L  U  M  R
V  M  A  M  A  D  Q  M  P  S  K  U
M  R  B  T  T  L  J  H  P  L  W  M
O  Z  I  R  C  R  O  T  S  A  P  F
D  S  E  N  A  T  O  R  I  B  U  S
```

shouting (abl.)	fishermen (gen.)
lesson (dat.)	senators (dat.)
customs (acc.)	fears (abl.)
orators (gen.)	virgin (acc.)
shepherd (nom.)	good will (gen.)

Lesson 19
WORD SEARCH

```
L  M  M  E  R  O  B  R  A  M  H  M  G
T  E  N  T  A  T  I  O  N  I  B  U  S
T  N  P  D  Y  C  J  E  P  W  S  Z  L
T  T  K  U  L  V  D  B  N  U  R  I  S
K  F  T  C  G  O  N  K  B  L  B  Z  I
J  W  F  I  T  B  C  I  R  E  H  T  T
V  L  N  S  Y  C  N  Q  R  M  G  Z  A
Q  T  U  C  P  O  B  T  K  W  R  C  T
Q  C  F  P  I  E  A  E  V  Z  M  S  I
Q  R  T  S  G  T  D  G  L  R  R  I  R
P  W  S  V  E  B  Q  U  G  O  N  N  A
N  A  V  S  R  R  Y  J  M  R  S  A  C
P  L  L  T  Q  K  K  K  R  W  Z  P  W
```

tree (acc.)

charity (gen.)

guard (abl.)

leader (dat.)

freedoms (nom.)

bread (gen.)

sufferings (abl.)

feet (gen.)

sun (abl.)

temptations (abl.)

	lectiones
lectioni	lectionibus
	lectionibus

panis	panes
panis	
	panes

solis	
soli	solibus
	solibus

timor	timores
timorem	timores

Derivatives Crossword

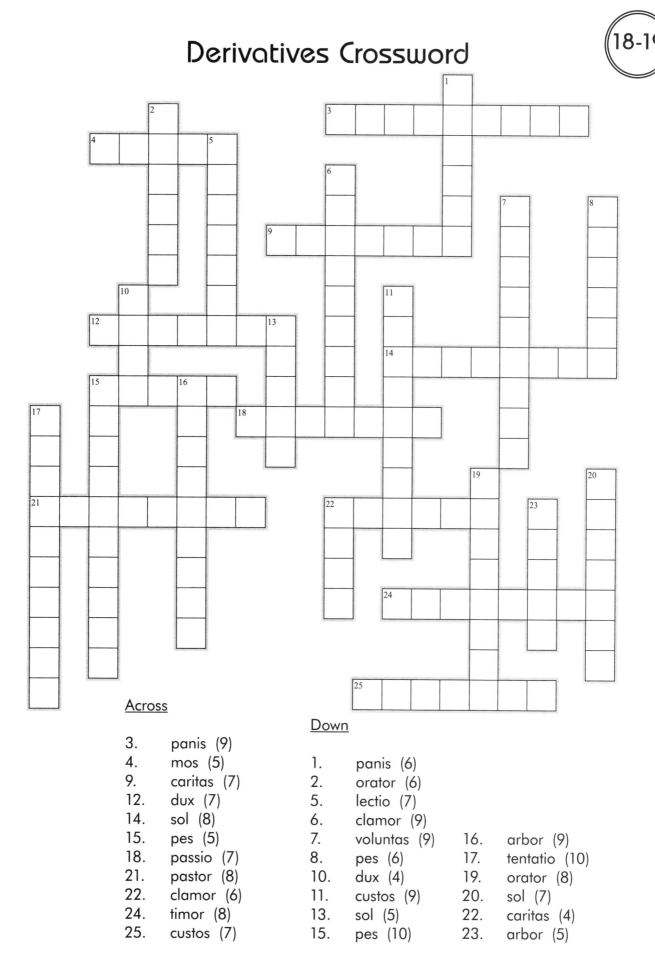

Across

3.   panis (9)
4.   mos (5)
9.   caritas (7)
12. dux (7)
14. sol (8)
15. pes (5)
18. passio (7)
21. pastor (8)
22. clamor (6)
24. timor (8)
25. custos (7)

Down

1.   panis (6)
2.   orator (6)
5.   lectio (7)
6.   clamor (9)
7.   voluntas (9)
8.   pes (6)
10. dux (4)
11. custos (9)
13. sol (5)
15. pes (10)

16. arbor (9)
17. tentatio (10)
19. orator (8)
20. sol (7)
22. caritas (4)
23. arbor (5)

Grammar Crossword

Across

6. (in) the sun (4)
10. shouting (dir. obj.) (8)
11. of suffering (9)
12. charity (subject) (7)
13. the orators (ind. obj.) (10)
14. (with) suffering (8)
16. of the fishermen (10)
18. shouting (subject) (6)
19. good will (ind. obj.) (9)
21. the sun (subject) (3)
22. (with) fears (9)
25. liberty (dir. obj.) (10)
27. shepherds (ind. obj.) (10)
28. bread (dir. obj.) (5)
32. (from) a lesson (8)
34. the leaders' (5)
35. (with) charity (8)
37. the virgin (dir. obj.) (8)
39. custom (subject) (3)
40. fears (subject) (7)
41. the trees (ind. obj.) (9)
43. fisherman (subject) (8)
45. charity (dir. obj.) (9)
48. suffering (subject) (6)
49. (by) feet (7)
50. liberty (subject) (8)
51. a shepherd (ind. obj.) (7)

Down

1. bread (subject) (5)
2. the senator (subject) (7)
3. the leaders (ind. obj.) (7)
4. (with) shouting (7)
5. fear (dir. obj.) (7)
6. senators (ind. obj.) (11)
7. of orators (8)
8. a virgin (subject) (5)
9. guard (subject) (6)
11. a foot (subject) (3)
12. the guards (dir. obj.) (8)
14. fishermen (subject) (10)
15. an orator (dir. obj.) (8)
17. (with) good will (9)
20. lessons (dir. obj.) (9)
23. (with) liberty (9)
24. a leader (subject) (3)
26. of the custom (5)
27. (with) bread (4)
29. of feet (5)
30. a guard (ind. obj.) (7)
31. of shepherds (8)
33. the senators' (9)
36. (in) lessons (11)
37. of the virgin (8)
38. of good will (10)
42. the tree's (7)
44. suns (subject) (5)
46. the tree (subject) (5)
47. (by) custom (4)

18-19

95

TRANSFORMER

1. Senator urbis nomen scit. (The senator knows the name of the city.)

_____ urbis nomen scit.

oratorem
dux
arbor

_____ urbis nomen _____ .

dicimus
venit
audit

_____ _____ nomen _____ .

custodis
piscatores
panis

_____ _____ _____ _____ .

pedem
solem
vocem

2. Arbores oppidi portam impediunt. (Trees are blocking the gate of the town.)

_____ oppidi portam impediunt.

equos
senatores
libertas

_____ oppidi portam _____ .

aperiunt
munit
veniunt

_____ _____ portam _____ .

lectionis
urbis
viam

_____ _____ _____ _____ .

ecclesias
fenestras
timores

PARSE STRINGS

pedis	adverb
sciebam	ablative singular
lectionem	nominative singular
sentiunt	1st person plural imperfect
cras	1st person singular imperfect
muniebamus	accusative singular
clamores	genitive plural
custodibus	genitive singular
aperis	dative singular
audiebant	3rd person plural present
sed	1st person plural present
more	2nd person singular present
lectio	dative plural
arborum	conjunction
duci	3rd person plural imperfect
venimus	accusative plural

Match Up

voluntary	snake
temptation	cool
lecture	din
liberty	disgust
arboreal	oppression
timorous	eclipse
clamor	required
solar	singer
passionate	palace
ducal	lewd
oratorio	confident
immoral	professor

Lesson 20
WORD SEARCH

S	U	B	I	N	I	F	B	G	T	Y
Y	S	F	C	H	H	K	K	C	T	N
W	I	D	B	T	S	J	K	L	I	M
A	D	W	G	I	B	Y	R	V	W	M
R	E	N	V	M	S	M	I	C	L	N
T	S	I	D	U	S	S	E	F	R	V
E	C	P	B	K	Q	E	R	N	Y	M
S	T	I	G	W	S	H	T	Y	T	N
Z	V	P	T	N	I	C	G	N	N	I
O	R	B	E	M	V	Q	F	D	E	B
G	N	Z	Q	K	A	J	P	B	L	D

arts (acc.)   mind (dat.)

bird (gen.)   snow (gen.)

citizen (nom.)   world (acc.)

teeth (nom.)   sheep (dat. pl.)

ends (abl.)   seat (gen.)

Lesson 21
WORD SEARCH

```
M  J  D  V  B  Y  R  V  M  G  P
S  A  C  T  J  U  O  P  E  R  A
U  K  R  Z  R  P  M  M  S  L  M
B  C  S  I  R  E  V  U  M  K  V
I  A  S  J  A  J  N  R  L  N  K
N  R  Q  T  B  L  P  E  N  L  V
I  M  R  N  U  G  K  N  M  N  X
M  I  Q  V  Y  C  D  I  R  C  X
U  N  S  A  L  E  R  T  R  F  L
L  I  Z  C  O  R  D  I  B  U  S
F  S  K  B  F  N  K  J  P  M  N
```

song (gen.)	works (acc.)
hearts (abl.)	countryside (gen.)
rivers (dat.)	salt (abl.)
journeys (gen.)	spring (gen.)
seas (nom.)	wound (acc.)

artis	
	artibus
artem	
	artibus

vulnus	
	vulnerum
vulneri	
vulnere	

	dentes
dentis	dentium
	dentes

civis	civium
	civibus
	civibus

Derivatives Crossword

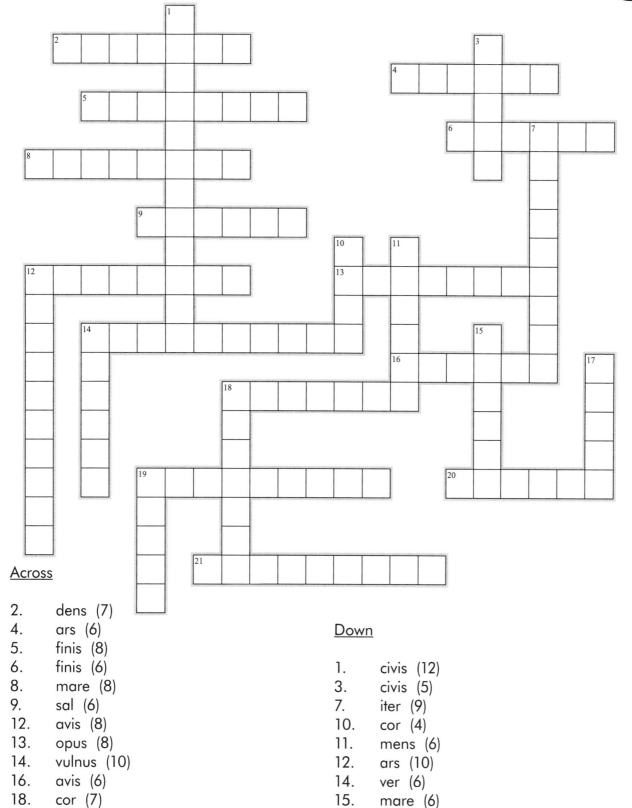

Across

2. dens (7)
4. ars (6)
5. finis (8)
6. finis (6)
8. mare (8)
9. sal (6)
12. avis (8)
13. opus (8)
14. vulnus (10)
16. avis (6)
18. cor (7)
19. opus (9)
20. dens (6)
21. sedes (9)

Down

1. civis (12)
3. civis (5)
7. iter (9)
10. cor (4)
11. mens (6)
12. ars (10)
14. ver (6)
15. mare (6)
17. rus (5)
18. cor (7)
19. orbis (5)

Grammar Crossword

Across

2. (in) snow (4)
4. songs (subject) (7)
6. of the mind (6)
12. (with) skill (4)
13. of the sea (5)
15. teeth (ind. obj.) (8)
16. wound (subject) (6)
17. the end (subject) (5)
20. the citizens (ind. obj.) (7)
21. the rivers (dir. obj.) (7)
22. a citizen's (5)
24. (with) birds (6)
26. a song (subject) (6)
29. teeth (dir. obj.) (6)
32. work (dir. obj.) (4)
33. a bird (dir. obj.) (4)
35. spring (subject) (3)
38. journey (subject) (4)
39. an end (dir. obj.) (5)
41. works (subject) (5)
43. the countryside (dir. obj.) (3)
44. journeys (dir. obj.) (7)
45. salt (dir. obj.) (5)
47. a bird's (4)
49. salt (subject) (3)
50. of the heart (6)

Down

1. of the citizens (6)
3. (by) a journey (7)
5. (from) the countryside (4)
6. the mind (subject) (4)
7. snow (subject) (3)
8. worlds (subject) (5)
9. the heart (ind. obj.) (5)
10. of the countryside (5)
11. sheep (pl.) (dir. obj.) (4)
14. (by) wounds (10)
15. tooth (subject) (4)
18. of snow (5)
19. a sheep (subject) (4)
21. (in) a river (7)
23. wounds (subject) (7)
24. art, skill (subject) (3)
25. the world's (5)
27. (from) spring (4)
28. (with) the mind (5)
30. (with) salt (4)
31. of songs (8)
32. the world (dir. obj.) (5)
34. (in) springs (7)
36. of the works (6)
37. the sea (dir. obj.) (4)
39. a river (subject) (6)
40. the seas (dir. obj.) (5)
41. a sheep (ind. obj.) (3)
42. (by) the ends (7)
46. the arts (dir. obj.) (5)
48. heart (subject) (3)

TRANSFORMER

1. Rex civium timorem sentit. (The king feels the fear of the citizens.)

Rex civium timorem _____.

puniunt
augebat
dormiebat

_____ civium timorem _____.

bellum
militum
sol

_____ civium _____ _____.

legem
passionis
clamorem

_____ _____ _____ _____.

urbis
campis
tela

2. Equus in via currit. (A horse is running in the road.)

Equus in _____ currit.

flumine
campo
urbium

_____ in _____ currit.

pastor
viri
canum

_____ in _____ _____.

sedebam
vidit
dormit

3. Urbis mores defendunt. (They defend the customs of the city.)

Urbis _____ defendunt.

portae
libertatem
poetarum

Urbis _____ _____.

timent
portamus
venio

_____ _____ _____.

hostibus
populi
mare

PARSE STRINGS

civi	nominative singular m.-f.
opera	genitive plural neuter
finibus	ablative singular m.-f.
dentes	ablative plural neuter
avis	nominative plural neuter
mare	dative singular m.-f.
itinerum	accusative singular m.-f.
mente	genitive singular neuter
sedem	genitive plural m.-f.
civium	ablative plural m.-f.
carminis	accusative singular neuter
flumine	accusative plural m.-f.
cordibus	ablative singular neuter

Match Up

cordial	country
vernal	intelligence
saline	resident
artificial	unprotected
avian	March
rural	welcoming
vulnerable	physical
itinerant	velocity
orbital	solution
mental	species

Lesson 22
WORD SEARCH

Z	E	A	B	Y	K	N	B
E	T	J	U	T	Z	M	E
U	I	U	U	T	I	Y	U
Q	A	M	I	T	E	V	Q
A	M	Z	A	D	B	M	I
T	Y	T	O	R	I	S	D
I	S	E	T	N	O	F	N
X	Z	W	I	R	U	J	U

however	right (dat.)
for a long time	mouth (gen.)
even	at once
fountains (acc.)	then
therefore	on all sides

Lesson 23
WORD SEARCH

```
D V G H T Q C X M X M S P
R C M Z B X K H W U H U F
K T Y U Q K N U T H T T
K L S K U L K T Q S H N N
T N U P B S A K P E L E K
L Y C K O T U I K N N V M
Y R A D I R R D L A U D Z
X N L U D I T X L T X A K
T C Q V T N J U E U N B P
M E W U G W R P M I L R M
H R S J M Y M T P R W P T
T J S U B I T C U R F Q Y
E X E R C I T I B U S M M
```

arrivals (nom.)

cavalries (gen.)

armies (dat.)

fruits (abl.)

attack (abl.)

lakes (nom.)

harbor (acc.)

senate (dat.)

spirit (gen.)

experiences (gen.)

senatus	
	senatibus
senatum	
	senatibus

impetus	impetus
impetum	impetus

	adventus
adventus	adventuum
	adventus

	fructibus
fructum	
fructu	fructibus

Derivatives Crossword

Across

3. fons (5)
5. portus (4)
8. fructus (5)
9. exercitus (8)
10. jus (4)
11. adventus (6)
14. spiritus (9)

Down

1. fons (4)
2. jus (6)
4. adventus (9)
6. os (7)
7. impetus (9)
12. os (4)
13. jus (4)

Grammar Crossword

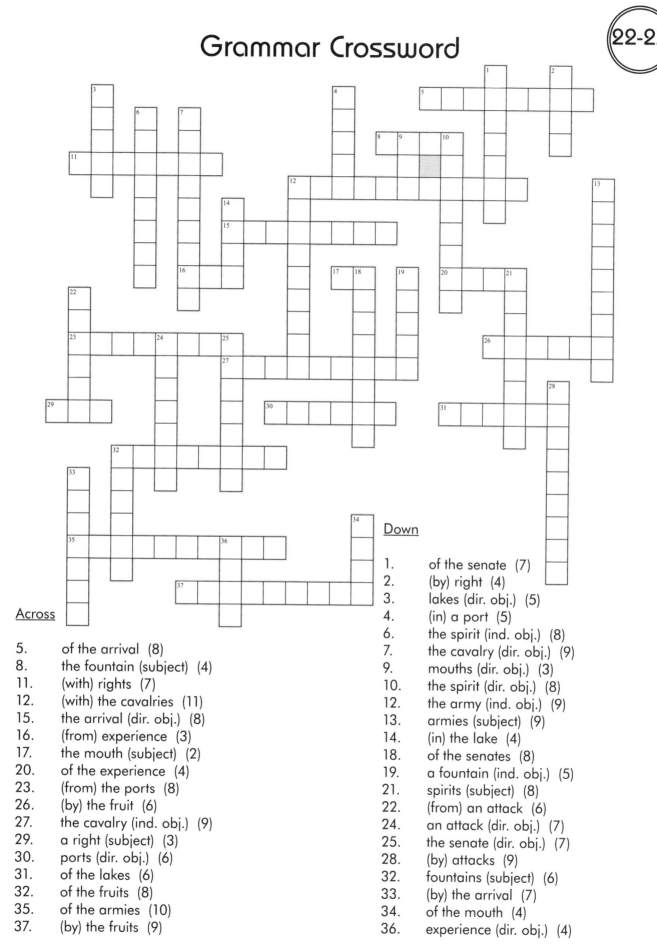

Across

5. of the arrival (8)
8. the fountain (subject) (4)
11. (with) rights (7)
12. (with) the cavalries (11)
15. the arrival (dir. obj.) (8)
16. (from) experience (3)
17. the mouth (subject) (2)
20. of the experience (4)
23. (from) the ports (8)
26. (by) the fruit (6)
27. the cavalry (ind. obj.) (9)
29. a right (subject) (3)
30. ports (dir. obj.) (6)
31. of the lakes (6)
32. of the fruits (8)
35. of the armies (10)
37. (by) the fruits (9)

Down

1. of the senate (7)
2. (by) right (4)
3. lakes (dir. obj.) (5)
4. (in) a port (5)
6. the spirit (ind. obj.) (8)
7. the cavalry (dir. obj.) (9)
9. mouths (dir. obj.) (3)
10. the spirit (dir. obj.) (8)
12. the army (ind. obj.) (9)
13. armies (subject) (9)
14. (in) the lake (4)
18. of the senates (8)
19. a fountain (ind. obj.) (5)
21. spirits (subject) (8)
22. (from) an attack (6)
24. an attack (dir. obj.) (7)
25. the senate (dir. obj.) (7)
28. (by) attacks (9)
32. fountains (subject) (6)
33. (by) the arrival (7)
34. of the mouth (4)
36. experience (dir. obj.) (4)

PARSE STRINGS

orum	genitive singular neuter
senatui	accusative plural neuter
lacus	accusative singular masculine
impetum	dative plural masculine
juris	ablative singular masculine
ore	dative singular masculine
fructuum	ablative singular neuter
portibus	genitive plural masculine
juribus	accusative plural masculine
ora	ablative plural neuter
jus	genitive plural neuter
exercitu	accusative singular neuter

Match Up

spirited	drill
impetuous	fair
usual	risky
adventurous	profitable
just	customary
exercise	lively
fruitful	hesitant

Lesson 24
WORD SEARCH

M	S	F	I	D	E	I
E	U	S	G	P	D	F
R	B	R	P	I	M	A
I	E	P	E	E	R	C
D	I	M	I	R	I	I
I	D	C	N	M	U	E
E	A	M	R	R	T	M

battle line (acc.)

days (abl.)

day (acc.)

face (acc.)

faith (dat.)

midday (abl.)

things (gen.)

hope (gen.)

Lesson 25
WORD SEARCH

```
Q  K  B  L  K  X  A  Y  M  J  W  C
S  I  N  E  I  L  A  U  S  D  Q  H
G  L  P  X  B  Y  R  M  I  W  Y  R
F  K  N  O  I  A  H  T  R  A  F  I
P  V  R  Q  D  M  K  M  A  R  R  S
R  U  K  I  J  X  L  F  L  E  X  T
M  O  P  M  W  C  Z  A  C  V  S  I
K  U  M  L  W  P  X  G  L  A  N  A
C  K  L  A  E  T  U  M  T  Q  Z  N
F  B  G  F  N  N  A  T  K  K  O
N  T  Y  Y  G  A  E  W  T  P  T  F
P  L  L  Y  F  B  Q  G  X  F  L  R
```

white (m. gen. pl.)

bright (f. dat. pl.)

foreign (n. dat. pl.)

eager (f. gen. pl.)

nurturing (m. gen. sing.)

happy (n. acc. sing.)

blessed (f. acc. pl.)

Roman (n. acc. pl.)

Christian (m. abl. sing.)

true (f. abl. sing.)

	vera
veri	verorum
	veris

res	res
rei	
	res

	laetae
laetae	laetis
	laetis

diei	
	diebus
diem	
	diebus

Derivatives Crossword

<u>Across</u>

1. facies (6)
5. fides (7)
8. clarus (7)
9. res (4)
11. cupidus (8)
13. spes (7)
16. meridies (8)
18. beatus (9)
19. dies (5)
20. facies (6)

<u>Down</u>

2. albus (6)
3. clarus (8)
4. alienus (8)
6. fides (8)
7. dies (4)
10. cupidus (5)
12. clarus (9)
13. spes (9)
14. alienus (5)
15. res (8)
17. verus (6)

Grammar Crossword

Across

3. duci __(eager)__ (6)
6. verbis __(true)__ (5)
7. juribus __(Roman)__ (7)
10. matribus __(nurturing)__ (5)
12. solem __(bright)__ (6)
13. the battle line (dir. obj.) (5)
15. carminibus __(happy)__ (6)
18. cordum __(true)__ (7)
23. (in) the face (5)
24. magistros __(happy)__ (6)
26. ducum __(foreign)__ (9)
28. panem __(blessed)__ (6)
29. of the face (6)
30. facie __(happy)__ (5)
31. days (dir. obj.) (4)
32. periculorum __(clear)__ (8)
35. of midday (8)
37. a day (dir. obj.) (4)
38. (by) things (5)
39. a face (dir. obj.) (6)
41. hope (subject) (4)
42. (with) loyalty (4)
43. senatorem __(eager)__ (7)
44. (with) the thing (2)
45. jus __(foreign)__ (7)
46. reginae __(eager)__ (7)

Down

1. pani __(white)__ (4)
2. of the things (5)
3. fidei __(Christian)__ (11)
4. nivis __(bright)__ (6)
5. nive __(white)__ (4)
8. hope (dir. obj.) (4)
9. of the battle line (5)
10. montibus __(white)__ (5)
11. (with) hope (3)
14. militum __(Christian)__ (13)
16. (in) a battle line (4)
17. nomina __(foreign)__ (6)
19. flumen __(Roman)__ (7)
20. midday (subject) (8)
21. libertatem __(true)__ (5)
22. nautam __(Christian)__ (11)
25. loyalty (subject) (5)
27. aquae __(blessed)__ (6)
29. loyalty (ind. obj.) (5)
33. amicos __(nurturing)__ (5)
34. midday (dir. obj.) (8)
36. of the days (6)
40. feminas __(Roman)__ (7)

121

TRANSFORMER

1. Rex alienus pacem petit. (A foreign king is seeking peace.)

Rex alienus _____ petit.

fructui
impetu
pecuniam

Rex _____ _____ petit.

beatum
cupidus
magna

Rex _____ _____ _____.

servat
dat
dicit

_____ _____ _____ _____.

regina
senator
homines

1. Pueri canem album habent. (The boys have a white dog.)

Pueri _____ album habent.

casam
equum
fluminis

Pueri _____ album _____ .

veniunt
vides
ducebant

Pueri _____ _____ _____.

laetum
magnos
bonam

_____ _____ _____ _____.

fratrem
agricolae
imperator

PARSE STRINGS

diebus	accusative singular feminine
laetos	genitive plural masculine
albarum	genitive singular neuter
faciem	accusative plural masculine
clari	accusative plural feminine
veris	dative singular feminine
spe	accusative singular masculine
aciei	dative plural neuter
res	dative singular masculine
beatum	ablative singular feminine
Romanorum	genitive plural feminine
cupido	ablative plural masculine

Match Up

cupidity	saint
despair	longitude
beatify	kingdom
fidelity	hopeless
meridian	treachery
clarity	generosity
alias	architecture
facade	obscurity
verify	sun
dial	confirm
republic	identity

ANSWER KEYS

Lesson 1

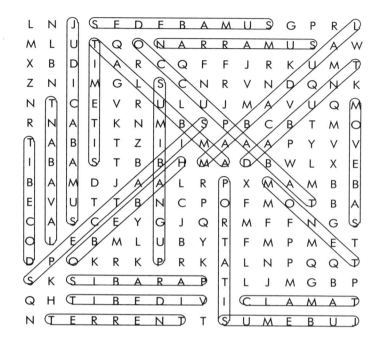

Lacunae

possum	possumus
potes	potestis
potest	possunt

habeo	habemus
habes	habetis
habet	habent

parabo	parabimus
parabis	parabitis
parabit	parabunt

timebam	timebamus
timebas	timebatis
timebat	timebant

Derivatives

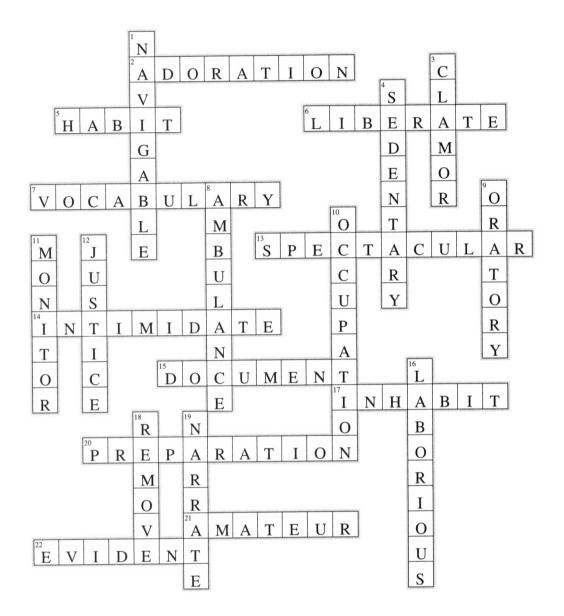

Grammar

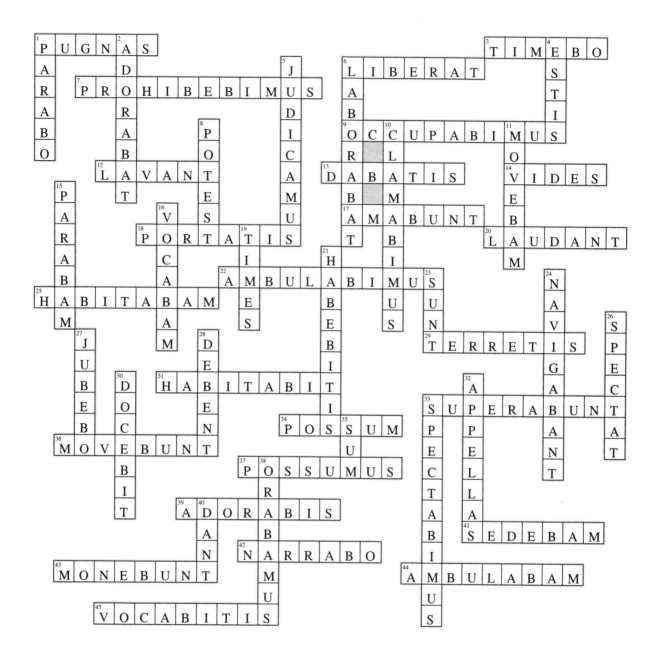

Match Up

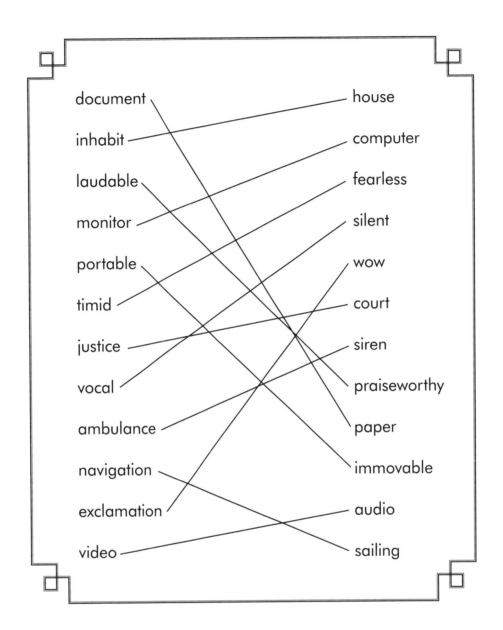

document	house
inhabit	computer
laudable	fearless
monitor	silent
portable	wow
timid	court
justice	siren
vocal	praiseworthy
ambulance	paper
navigation	immovable
exclamation	audio
video	sailing

Lesson 2

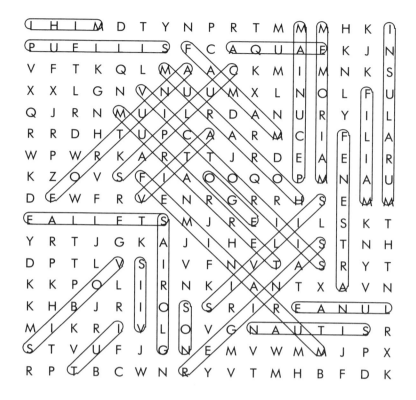

Lacunae

insula	insulae
insulae	insularum
insulae	insulis
insulam	insulas
insula	insulis

ego	nos
mei	nostri, nostrum
mihi	nobis
me	nos
me	nobis

tu	vos
tui	vestri, vestrum
tibi	vobis
te	vos
te	vobis

aqua	aquae
aquae	aquarum
aquae	aquis
aquam	aquas
aqua	aquis

Derivatives

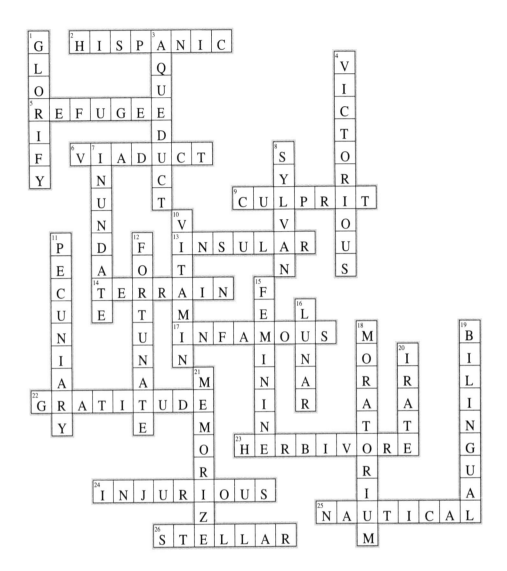

Grammar

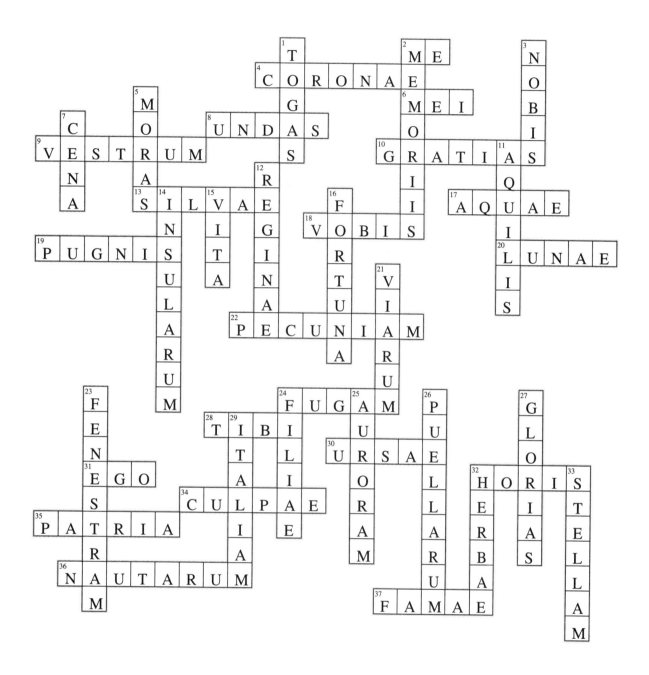

Transformer

1. Femina togam videt.
   Nauta togam videt.
   Nauta insulam videt.

2. Italia pecuniam habet.
   Regina pecuniam habet.
   Regina pecuniam amat.

3. Filiae fenestram lavant.
   Filiae mensam lavant.
   Filiae mensam movent.

Parse Strings

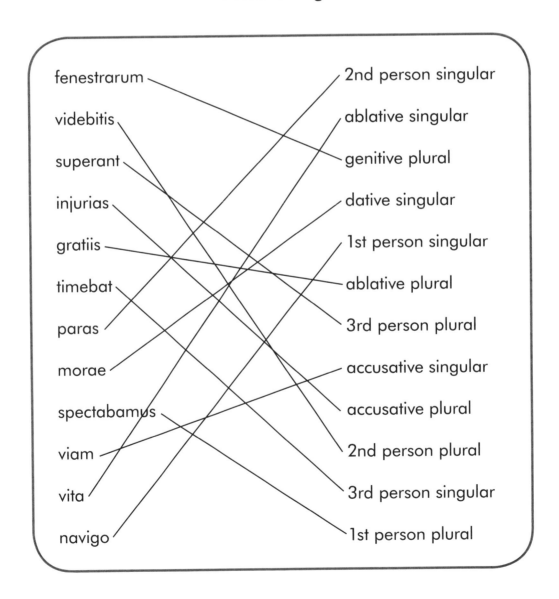

Match Up

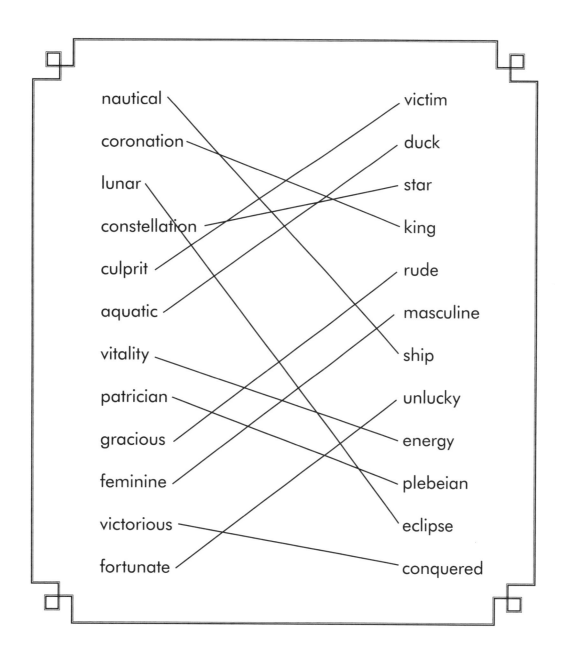

nautical

coronation

lunar

constellation

culprit

aquatic

vitality

patrician

gracious

feminine

victorious

fortunate

victim

duck

star

king

rude

masculine

ship

unlucky

energy

plebeian

eclipse

conquered

Lesson 3

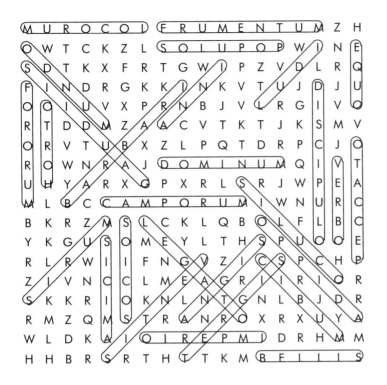

Lacunae

signum	signa
signi	signorum
signo	signis
signum	signa
signo	signis

gladius	gladii
gladii	gladiorum
gladio	gladiis
gladium	gladios
gladio	gladiis

hortus	horti
horti	hortorum
horto	hortis
hortum	hortos
horto	hortis

auxilium	auxilia
auxilii	auxiliorum
auxilio	auxiliis
auxilium	auxilia
auxilio	auxiliis

Derivatives

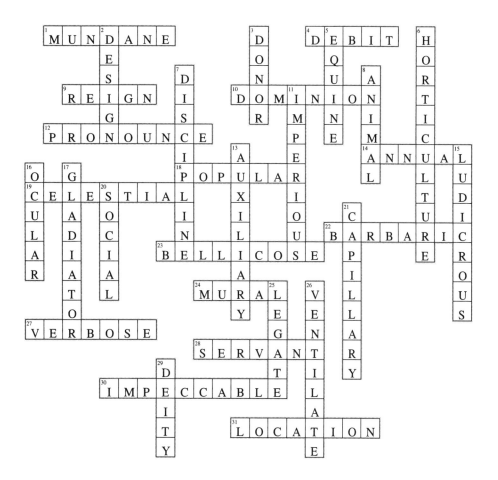

Grammar

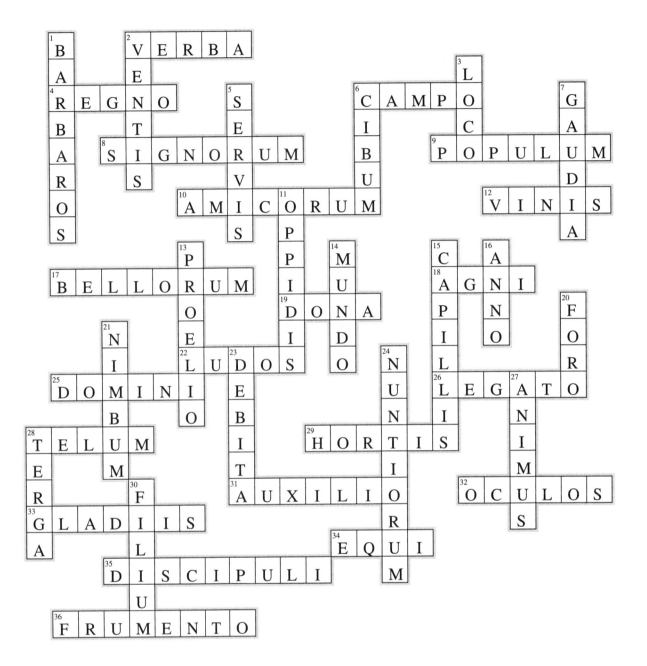

Transformer

1. Populus signum dabit.
   Populus signum videbat.
   Barbarus signum videbat.

2. Filius equos spectabat.
   Filius hortum spectabat.
   Filius hortum parabit.

3. Equi aquam habent.
   Equi aquam vident.
   Equi agnos vident.

Match Up

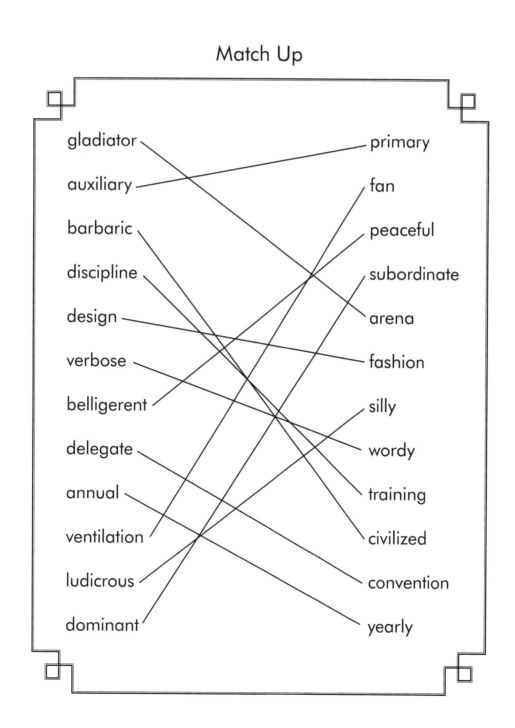

gladiator   primary

auxiliary   fan

barbaric   peaceful

discipline   subordinate

design   arena

verbose   fashion

belligerent   silly

delegate   wordy

annual   training

ventilation   civilized

ludicrous   convention

dominant   yearly

Lesson 4

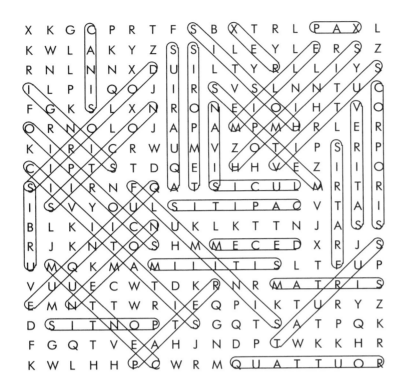

Derivatives

Grammar

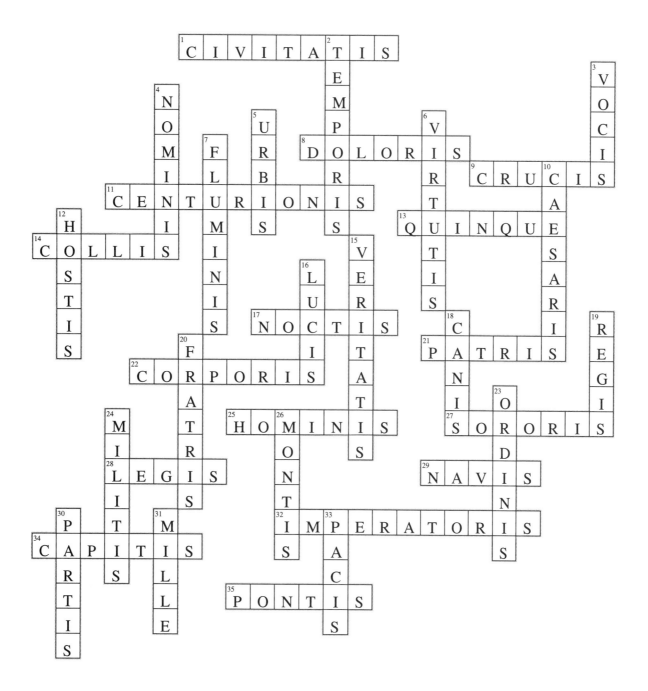

Transformer

1. Miles frumentum portat.
   Miles frumentum lavabat
   Centurio frumentum lavabat.

2. Rex gladium habet.
   Rex regnum habet.
   Rex regnum occupabit.

3. Regina equos timet.
   Canis equos timet.
   Canis ursam timet.

Parse Strings

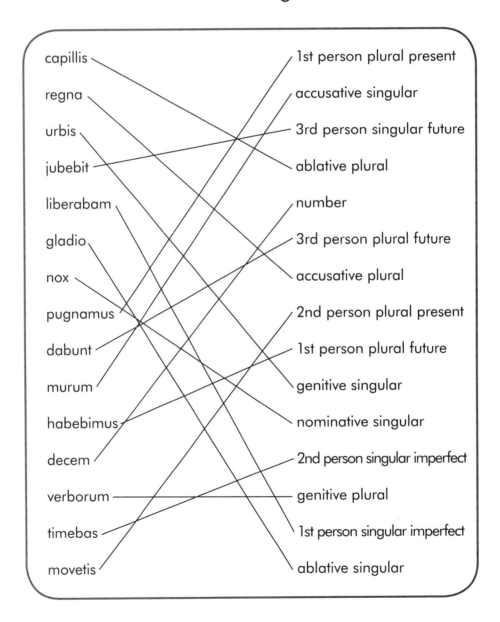

capillis

regna

urbis

jubebit

liberabam

gladio

nox

pugnamus

dabunt

murum

habebimus

decem

verborum

timebas

movetis

1st person plural present

accusative singular

3rd person singular future

ablative plural

number

3rd person plural future

accusative plural

2nd person plural present

1st person plural future

genitive singular

nominative singular

2nd person singular imperfect

genitive plural

1st person singular imperfect

ablative singular

Match Up

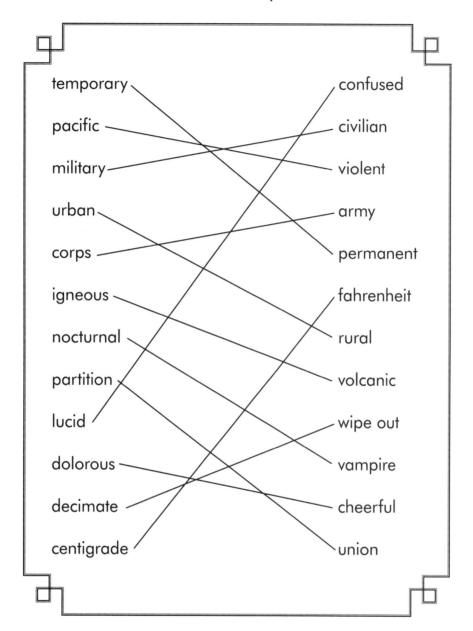

temporary — permanent
pacific — violent
military — civilian
urban — rural
corps — army
igneous — volcanic
nocturnal — vampire
partition — union
lucid — confused
dolorous — cheerful
decimate — wipe out
centigrade — fahrenheit

Lesson 5

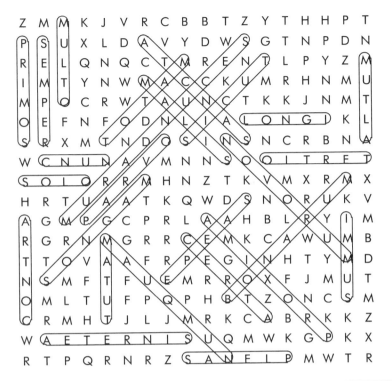

Lacunae

malum	mala
mali	malorum
malo	malis
malum	mala
malo	malis

longa	longae
longae	longarum
longae	longis
longam	longas
longa	longis

mea	meae
meae	mearum
meae	meis
meam	meas
mea	meis

novus	novi
novi	novorum
novo	novis
novum	novos
novo	novis

Derivatives

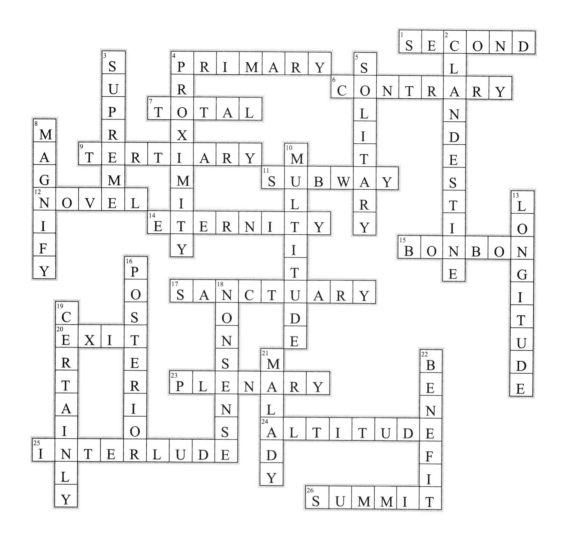

Grammar

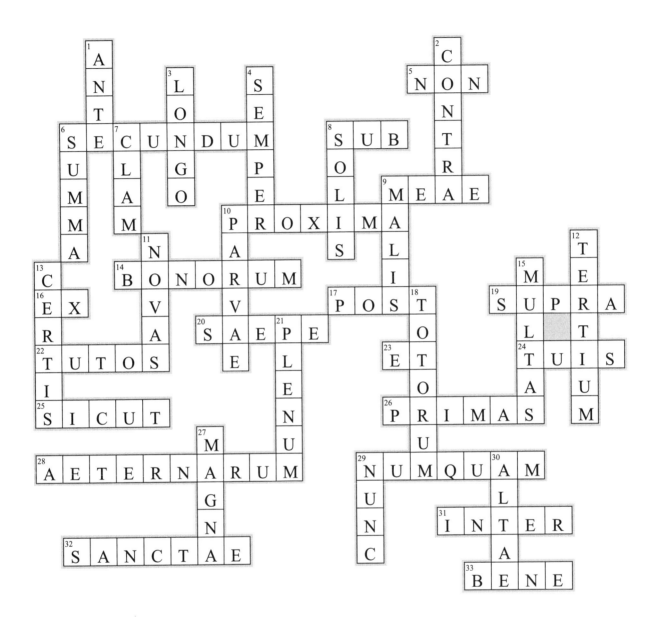

Parse Strings

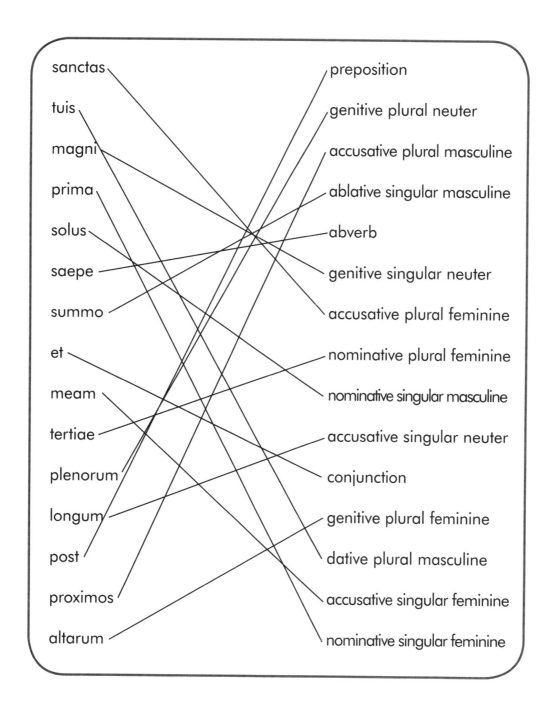

sanctas

tuis

magni

prima

solus

saepe

summo

et

meam

tertiae

plenorum

longum

post

proximos

altarum

preposition

genitive plural neuter

accusative plural masculine

ablative singular masculine

abverb

genitive singular neuter

accusative plural feminine

nominative plural feminine

nominative singular masculine

accusative singular neuter

conjunction

genitive plural feminine

dative plural masculine

accusative singular feminine

nominative singular feminine

Match Up

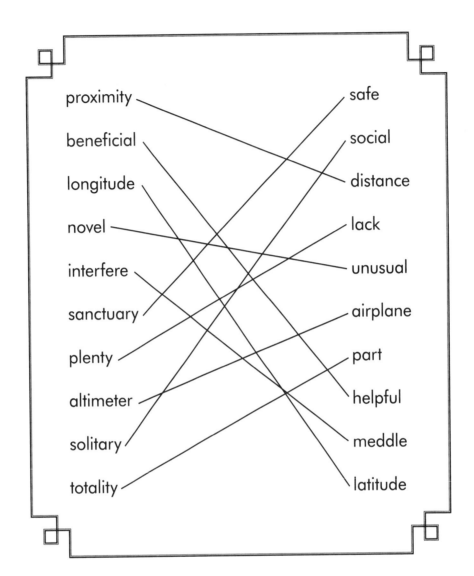

proximity   safe

beneficial   social

longitude   distance

novel   lack

interfere   unusual

sanctuary   airplane

plenty   part

altimeter   helpful

solitary   meddle

totality   latitude

Lessons 6-7

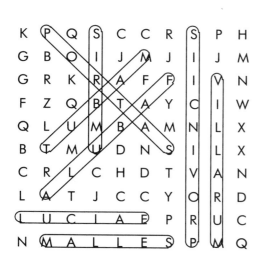

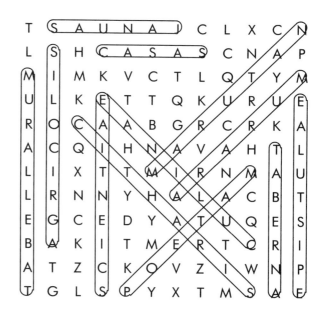

Lacunae

fabula	fabulae
fabulae	fabularum
fabulae	fabulis
fabulam	fabulas
fabula	fabulis

tabella	tabellae
tabellae	tabellarum
tabellae	tabellis
tabellam	tabellas
tabella	tabellis

agricola	agricolae
agricolae	agricolarum
agricolae	agricolis
agricolam	agricolas
agricola	agricolis

sella	sellae
sellae	sellarum
sellae	sellis
sellam	sellas
sella	sellis

Derivatives

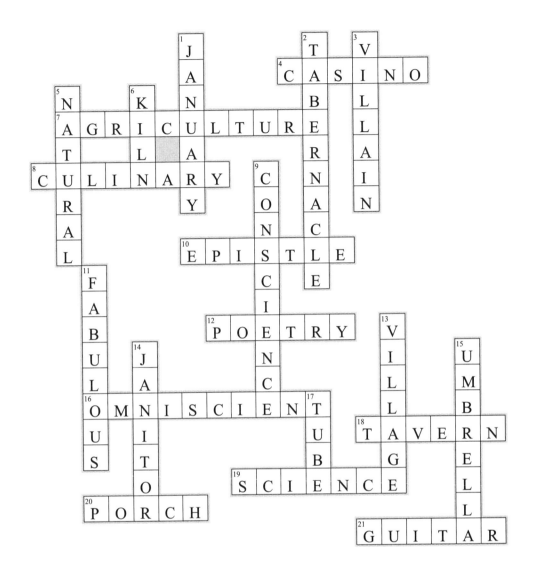

Grammar

Match Up

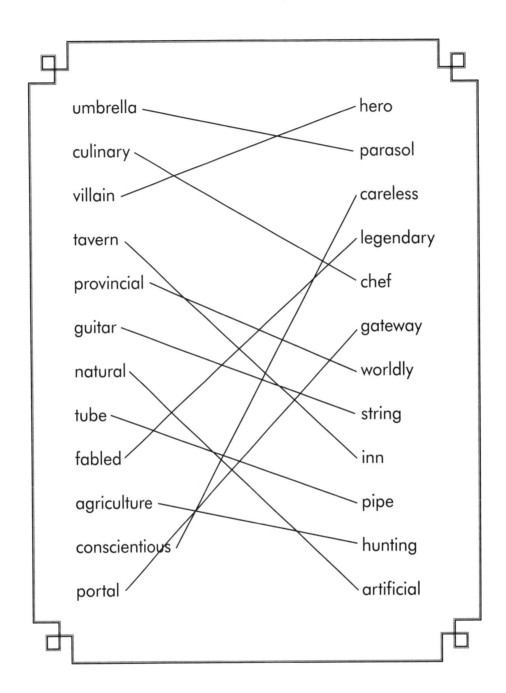

umbrella

culinary

villain

tavern

provincial

guitar

natural

tube

fabled

agriculture

conscientious

portal

hero

parasol

careless

legendary

chef

gateway

worldly

string

inn

pipe

hunting

artificial

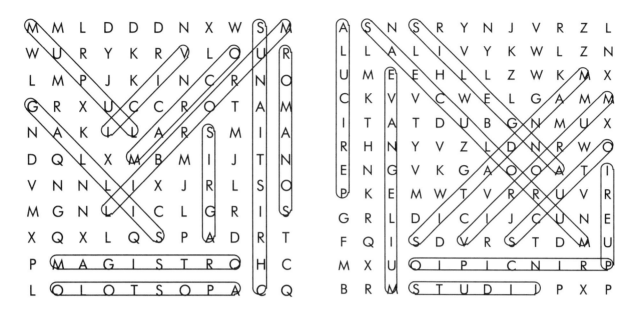

Lacunae

principium	principia
principii	principiorum
principio	principiis
principium	principia
principio	principiis

vicus	vici
vici	vicorum
vico	vicis
vicum	vicos
vico	vicis

studium	studia
studii	studiorum
studio	studiis
studium	studia
studio	studiis

liber	libri
libri	librorum
libro	libris
librum	libros
libro	libris

Derivatives

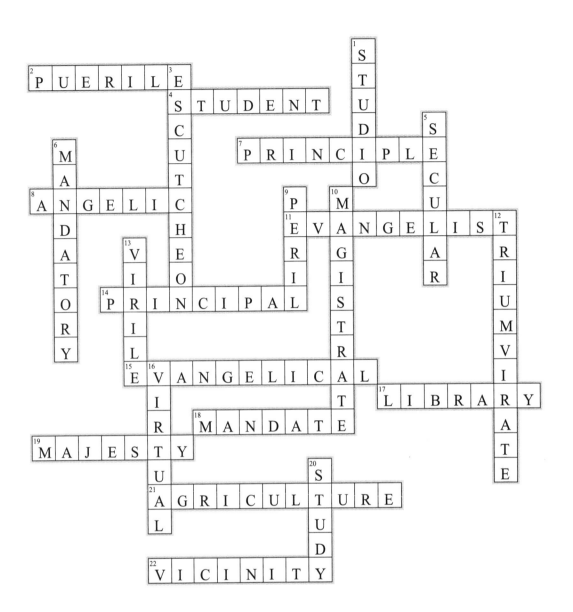

Grammar

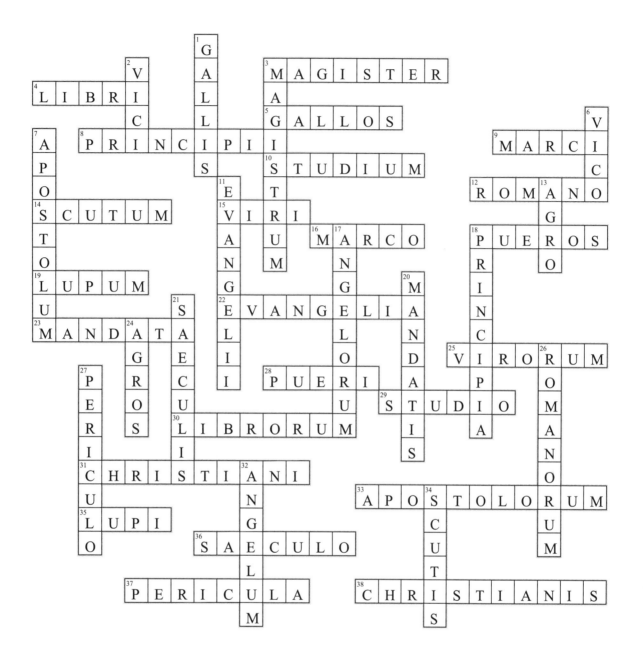

Parse Strings

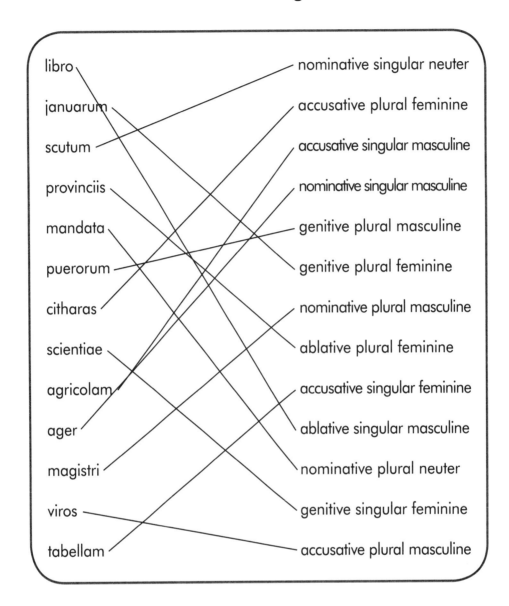

libro	nominative singular neuter
januarum	accusative plural feminine
scutum	accusative singular masculine
provinciis	nominative singular masculine
mandata	genitive plural masculine
puerorum	genitive plural feminine
citharas	nominative plural masculine
scientiae	ablative plural feminine
agricolam	accusative singular feminine
ager	ablative singular masculine
magistri	nominative plural neuter
viros	genitive singular feminine
tabellam	accusative plural masculine

Match Up

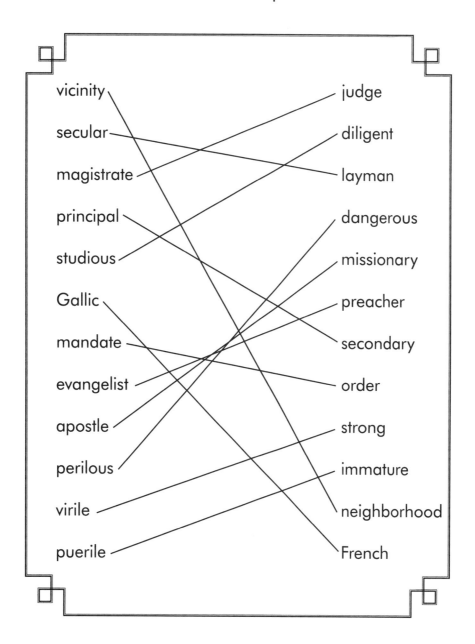

vicinity

secular

magistrate

principal

studious

Gallic

mandate

evangelist

apostle

perilous

virile

puerile

judge

diligent

layman

dangerous

missionary

preacher

secondary

order

strong

immature

neighborhood

French

Lessons 10-11

Derivatives

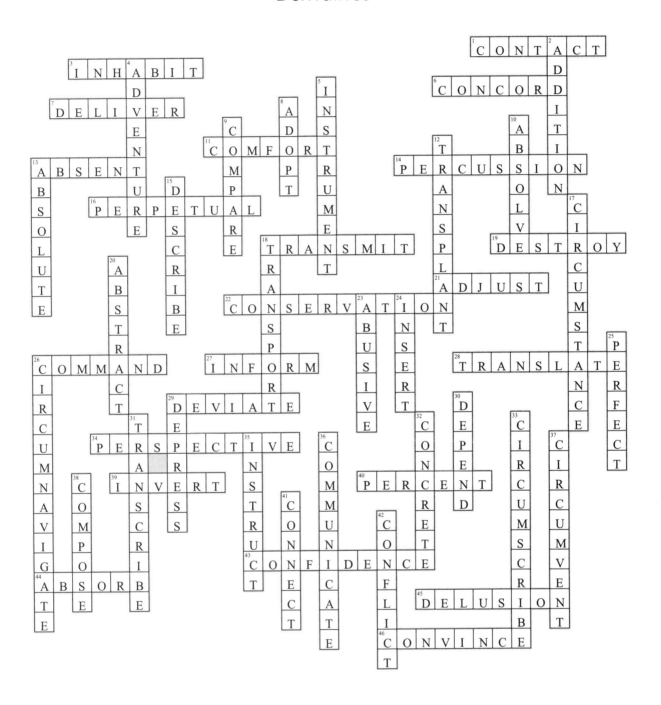

Grammar

Lessons 12-13

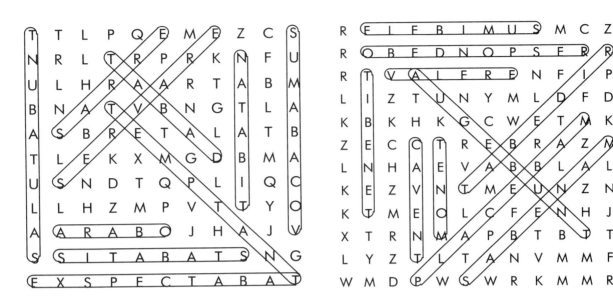

Lacunae

tenebam	tenebamus
tenebas	tenebatis
tenebat	tenebant

augebo	augebimus
augebis	augebitis
augebit	augebunt

sto	stamus
stas	statis
stat	stant

eram	eramus
eras	eratis
erat	erant

do	damus
das	datis
dat	dant

Derivatives

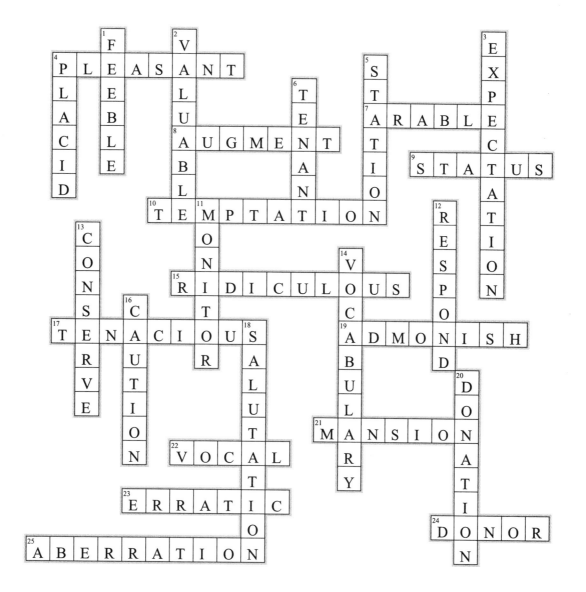

Grammar

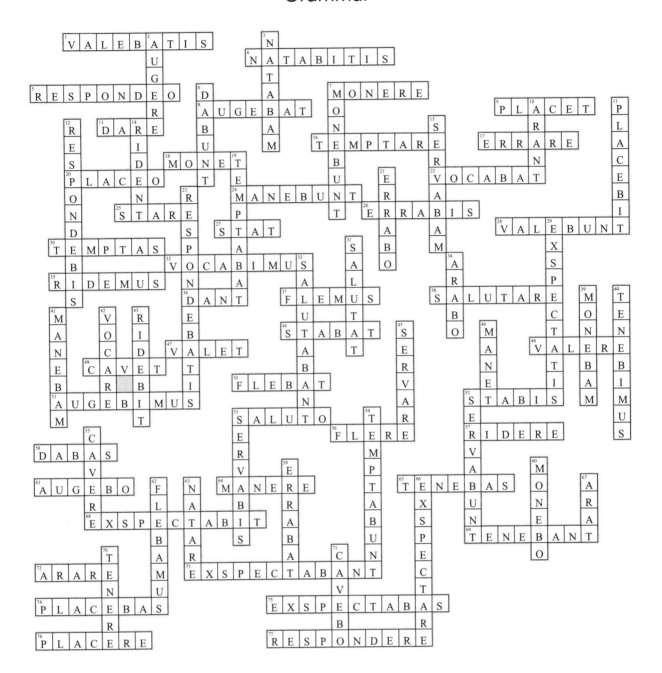

Transformer

1. Agricolae in villa laborant.
   Agricolae in agris laborant.
   Viri in agris laborant.

2. Canis circum insulam ambulabat.
   Nauta circum insulam ambulabat.
   Nauta circum insulam navigabat.

3. Imperator nuntium exspectabat.
   Imperator nuntium cavebat.
   Populus nuntium cavebat.

Parse Strings

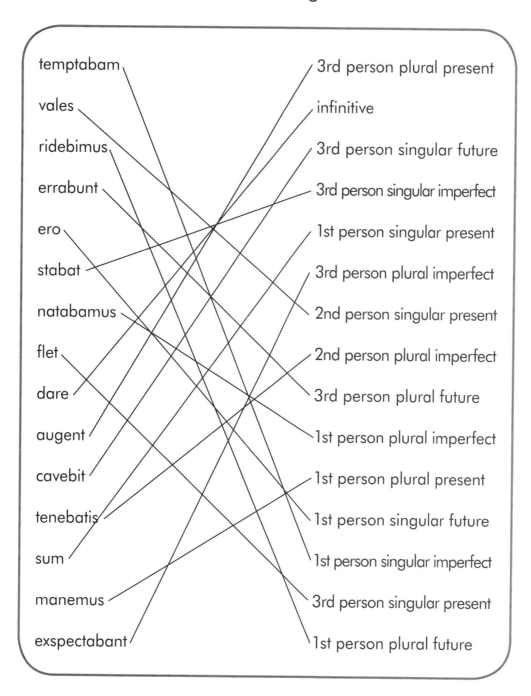

temptabam

vales

ridebimus

errabunt

ero

stabat

natabamus

flet

dare

augent

cavebit

tenebatis

sum

manemus

exspectabant

3rd person plural present

infinitive

3rd person singular future

3rd person singular imperfect

1st person singular present

3rd person plural imperfect

2nd person singular present

2nd person plural imperfect

3rd person plural future

1st person plural imperfect

1st person plural present

1st person singular future

1st person singular imperfect

3rd person singular present

1st person plural future

Match Up

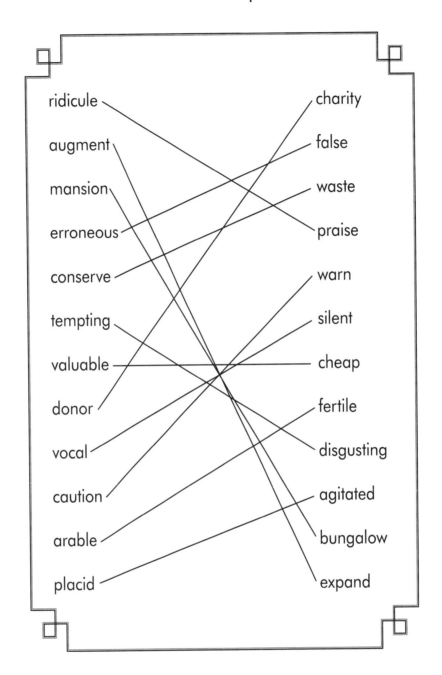

ridicule   charity

augment   false

mansion   waste

erroneous   praise

conserve   warn

tempting   silent

valuable   cheap

donor   fertile

vocal   disgusting

caution   agitated

arable   bungalow

placid   expand

Lessons 14-15

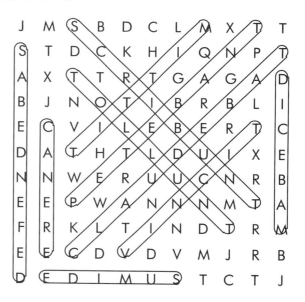

Lacunae

mittebam	mittebamus
mittebas	mittebatis
mittebat	mittebant

vivo	vivimus
vivis	vivitis
vivit	vivunt

rego	regimus
regis	regitis
regit	regunt

agebam	agebamus
agebas	agebatis
agebat	agebant

pono	ponimus
ponis	ponitis
ponit	ponunt

Derivatives

Grammar

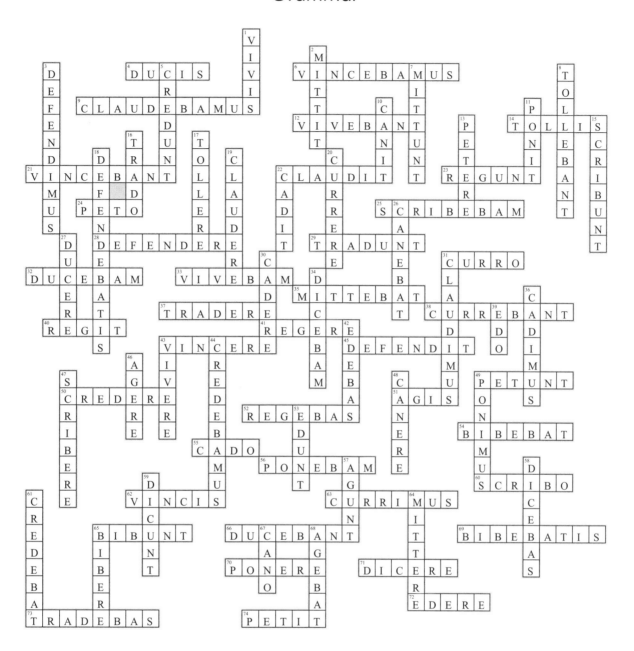

Transformer

1. Marcus trans viam currit.
   Marcus trans vicum currit.
   Marcus ad vicum currit.
   Puer ad vicum currit.

2. Poeta proelii fabulam canit.
   Poeta proelii fabulam scribit.
   Imperator proelii fabulam scribit.
   Imperator proelii famam scribit.

Parse Strings

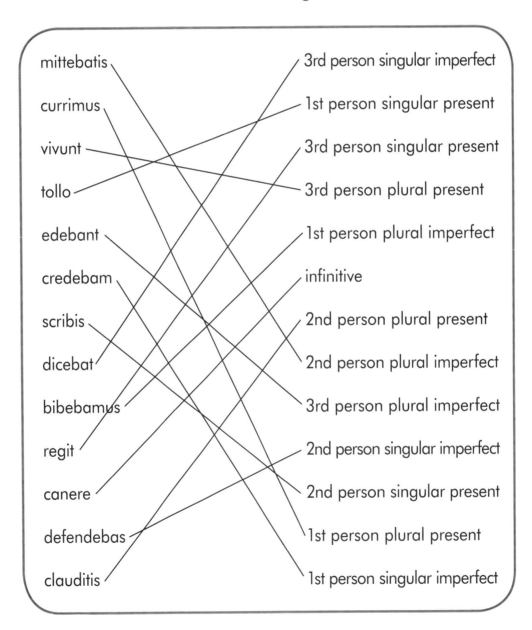

Match Up

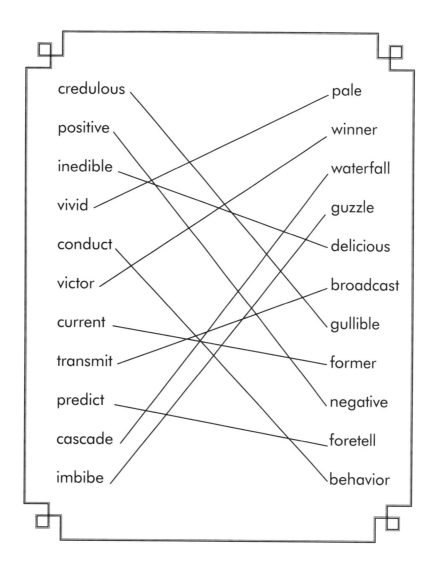

credulous

positive

inedible

vivid

conduct

victor

current

transmit

predict

cascade

imbibe

pale

winner

waterfall

guzzle

delicious

broadcast

gullible

former

negative

foretell

behavior

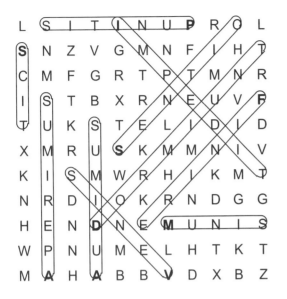

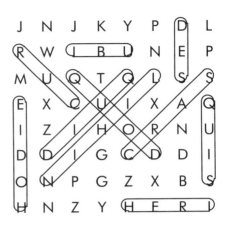

Lacunae

puniebam	puniebamus
puniebas	puniebatis
puniebat	puniebant

aperio	aperimus
aperis	aperitis
aperit	aperiunt

scio	scimus
scis	scitis
scit	sciunt

sentiebam	sentiebamus
sentiebas	sentiebatis
sentiebat	sentiebant

finio	finimus
finis	finitis
finit	finiunt

Derivatives

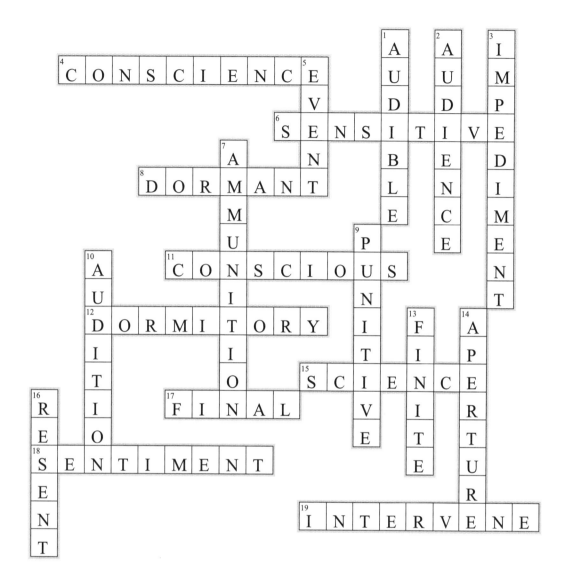

Grammar

Match Up

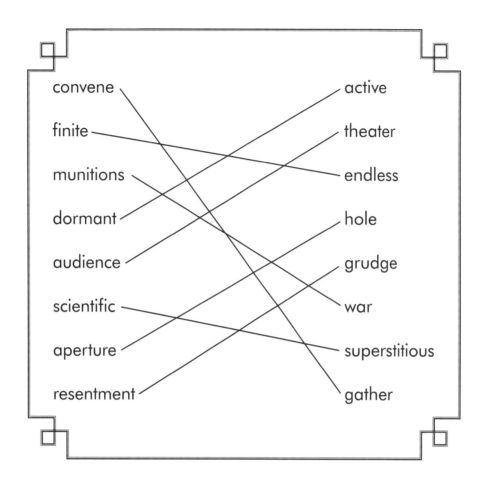

convene   active

finite   theater

munitions   endless

dormant   hole

audience   grudge

scientific   war

aperture   superstitious

resentment   gather

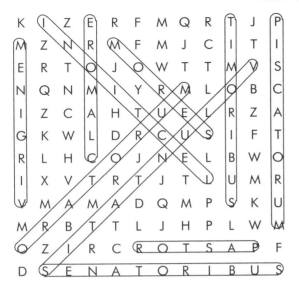
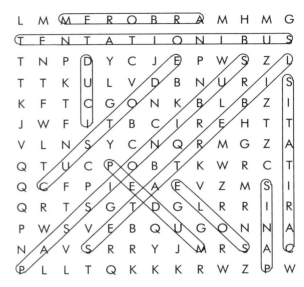

Lacunae

lectio	lectiones
lectionis	lectionum
lectioni	lectionibus
lectionem	lectiones
lectione	lectionibus

panis	panes
panis	panum
pani	panibus
panem	panes
pane	panibus

sol	soles
solis	solum
soli	solibus
solem	soles
sole	solibus

timor	timores
timoris	timorum
timori	timoribus
timorem	timores
timore	timoribus

Derivatives

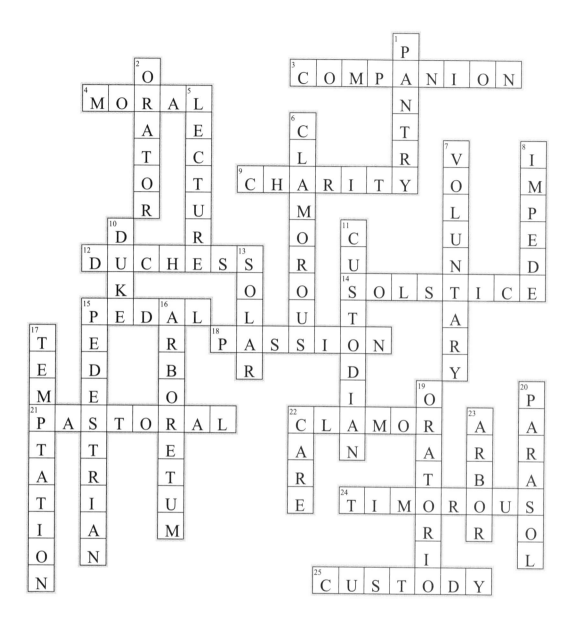

Grammar

Transformer

1. Dux urbis nomen scit.
   Dux urbis nomen audit.
   Dux custodis nomen audit.
   Dux custodis vocem audit.

2. Senatores oppidi portam impediunt.
   Senatores oppidi portam aperiunt.
   Senatores urbis portam aperiunt.
   Senatores urbis ecclesias aperiunt.

Parse Strings

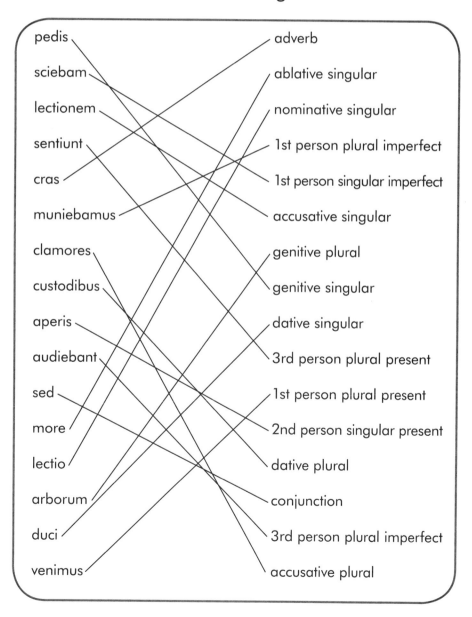

pedis
sciebam
lectionem
sentiunt
cras
muniebamus
clamores
custodibus
aperis
audiebant
sed
more
lectio
arborum
duci
venimus

adverb
ablative singular
nominative singular
1st person plural imperfect
1st person singular imperfect
accusative singular
genitive plural
genitive singular
dative singular
3rd person plural present
1st person plural present
2nd person singular present
dative plural
conjunction
3rd person plural imperfect
accusative plural

Match Up

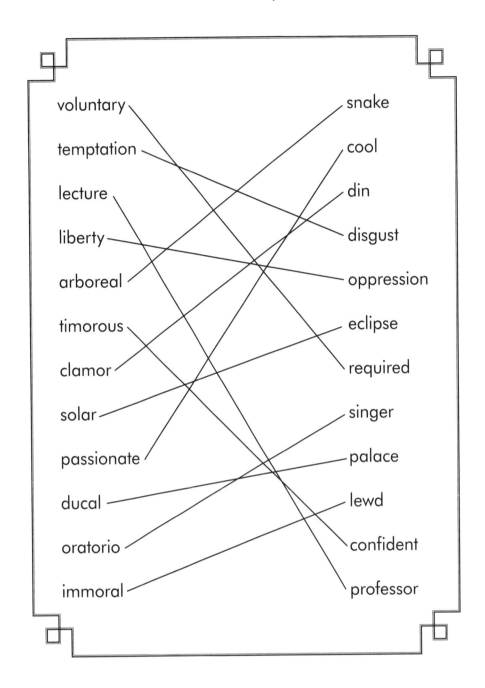

voluntary

temptation

lecture

liberty

arboreal

timorous

clamor

solar

passionate

ducal

oratorio

immoral

snake

cool

din

disgust

oppression

eclipse

required

singer

palace

lewd

confident

professor

Lessons 20-21

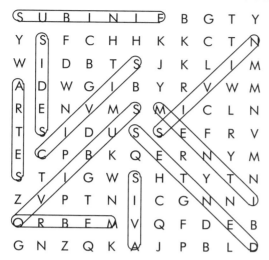
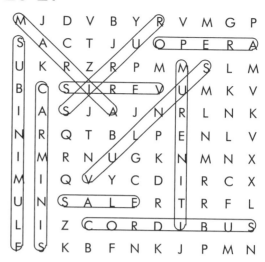

Lacunae

ars	artes
artis	artium
arti	artibus
artem	artes
arte	artibus

vulnus	vulnera
vuleris	vulnerum
vulneri	vulneribus
vulnus	vulnera
vulnere	vulneribus

dens	dentes
dentis	dentium
denti	dentibus
dentem	dentes
dente	dentibus

civis	cives
civis	civium
civi	civibus
civem	cives
cive	civibus

Derivatives

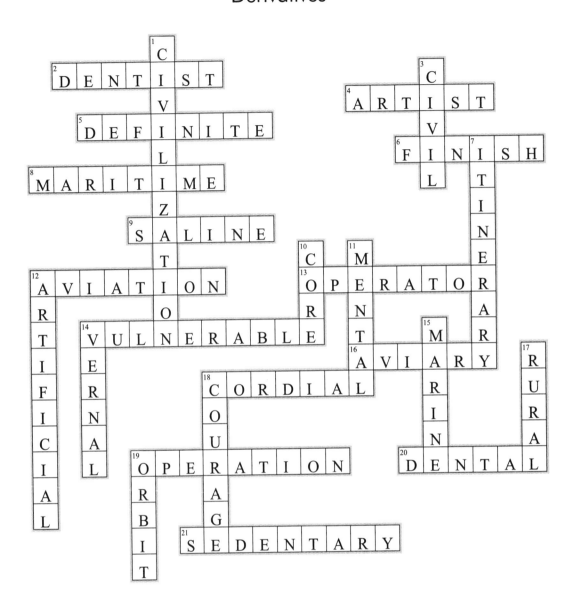

Grammar

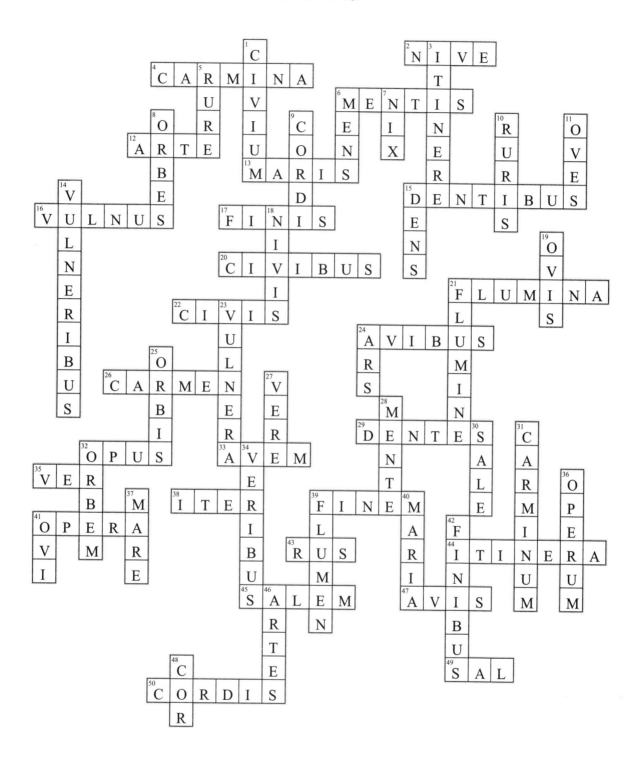

Transformer

1. Rex civium timorem augebat.
   Bellum civium timorem augebat.
   Bellum civium clamorem augebat.
   Bellum urbis clamorem augebat.

2. Equus in campo currit.
   Pastor in campo currit.
   Pastor in campo dormit.

3. Urbis libertatem defendunt.
   Urbis libertatem timent.
   Populi libertatem timent.

Parse Strings

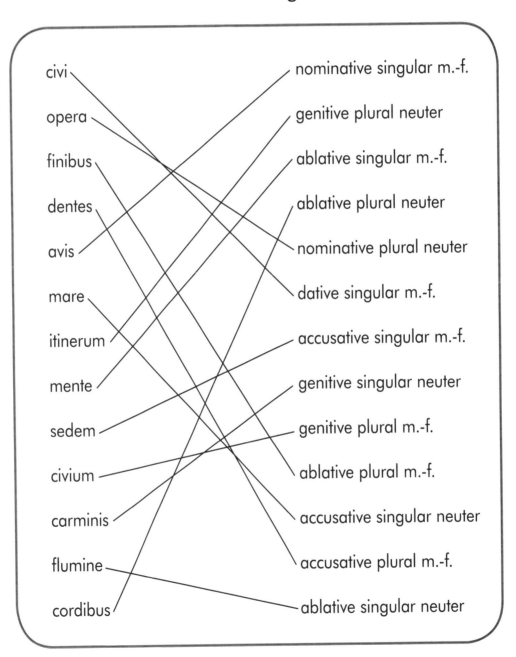

civi

opera

finibus

dentes

avis

mare

itinerum

mente

sedem

civium

carminis

flumine

cordibus

nominative singular m.-f.

genitive plural neuter

ablative singular m.-f.

ablative plural neuter

nominative plural neuter

dative singular m.-f.

accusative singular m.-f.

genitive singular neuter

genitive plural m.-f.

ablative plural m.-f.

accusative singular neuter

accusative plural m.-f.

ablative singular neuter

Match Up

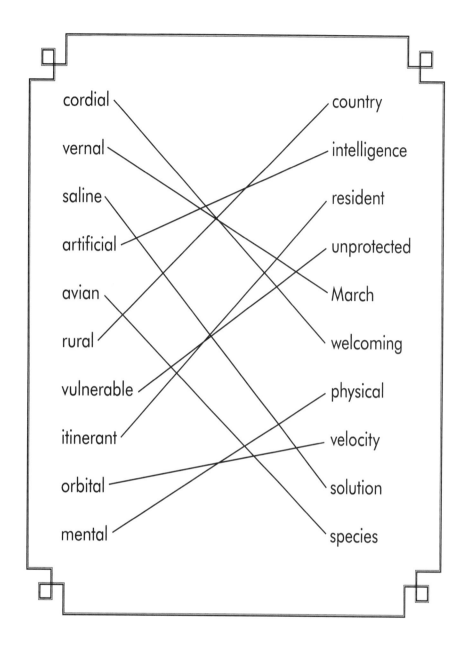

cordial   country

vernal   intelligence

saline   resident

artificial   unprotected

avian   March

rural   welcoming

vulnerable   physical

itinerant   velocity

orbital   solution

mental   species

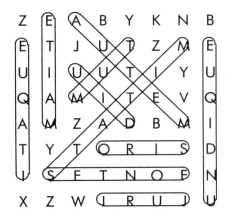

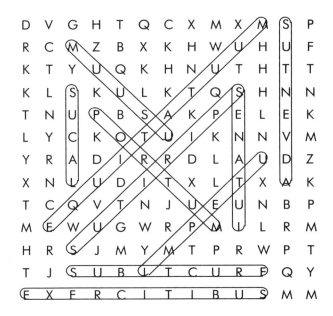

Lacunae

senatus	senatus
senatus	senatuum
senatui	senatibus
senatum	senatus
senatu	senatibus

impetus	impetus
impetus	impetuum
impetui	impetibus
impetum	impetus
impetu	impetibus

adventus	adventus
adventus	adventuum
adventui	adventibus
adventum	adventus
adventu	adventibus

fructus	fructus
fructus	fructuum
fructui	fructibus
fructum	fructus
fructu	fructibus

Derivatives

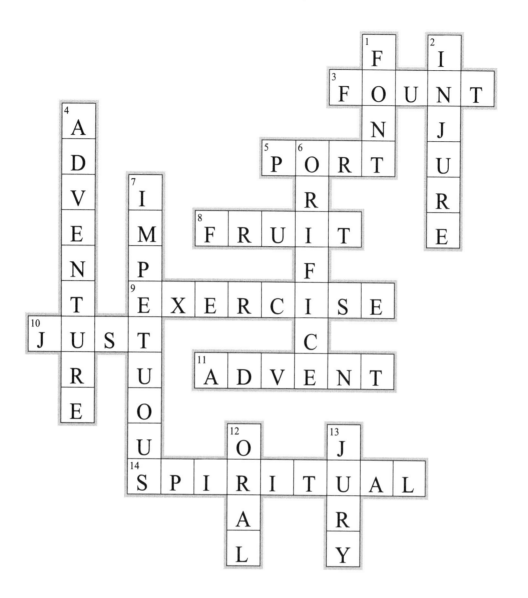

Grammar

Parse Strings

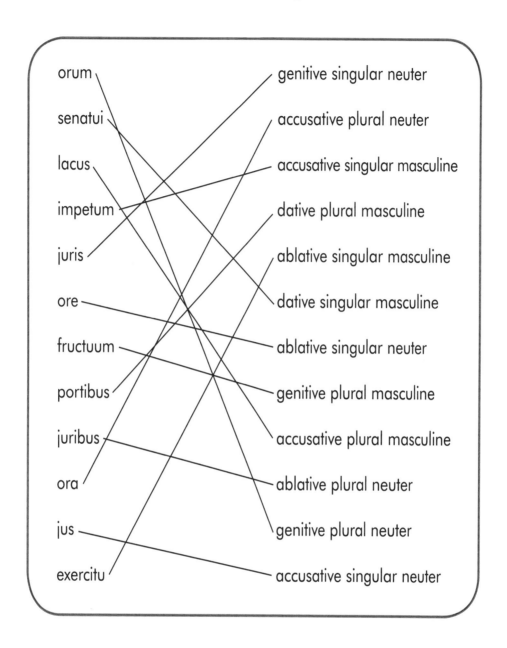

Match Up

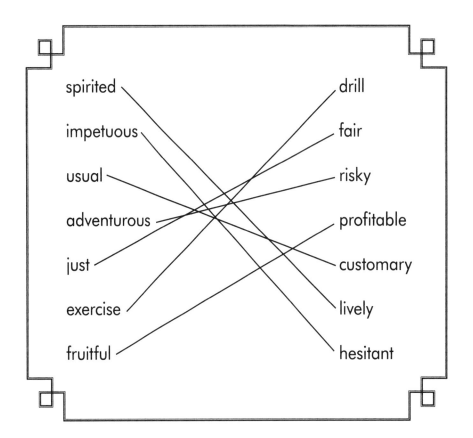

spirited

impetuous

usual

adventurous

just

exercise

fruitful

drill

fair

risky

profitable

customary

lively

hesitant

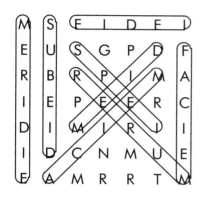

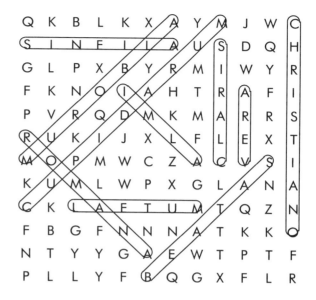

Lacunae

verum	vera
veri	verorum
vero	veris
verum	vera
vero	veris

res	res
rei	rerum
rei	rebus
rem	res
re	rebus

laeta	laetae
laetae	laetarum
laetae	laetis
laetam	laetas
laeta	laetis

dies	dies
diei	dierum
diei	diebus
diem	dies
die	diebus

Derivatives

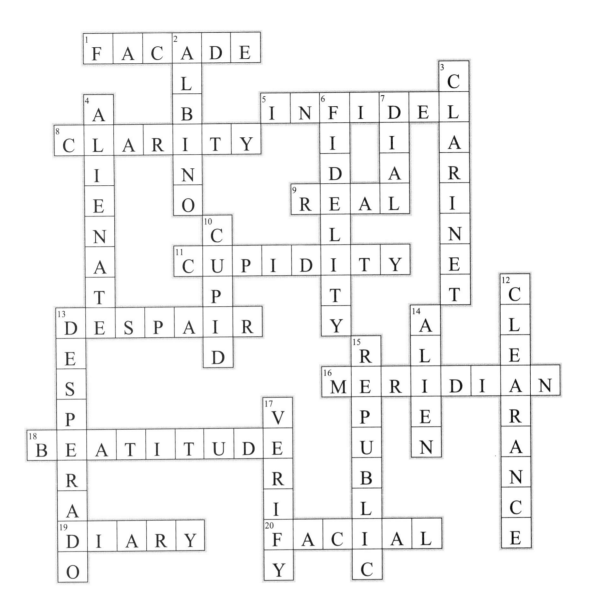

Grammar

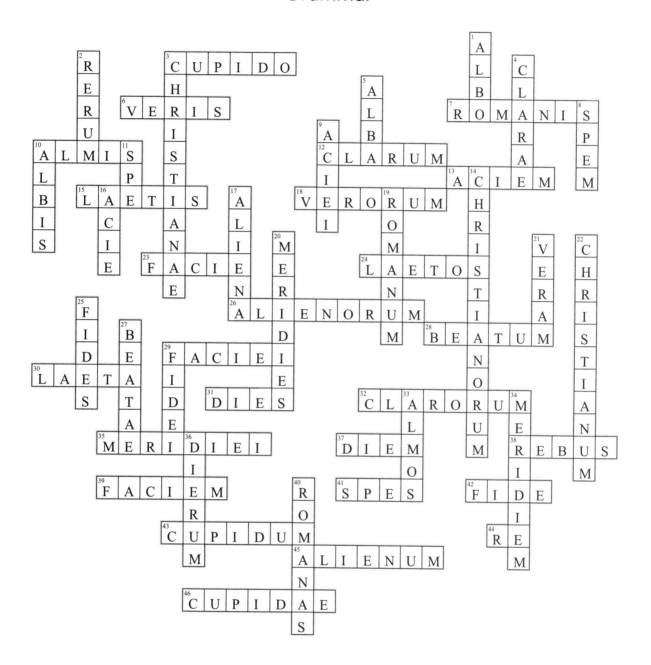

Transformer

1. Rex alienus pecuniam petit.
   Rex cupidus pecuniam petit.
   Rex cupidus pecuniam servat.
   Senator cupidus pecuniam servat.

2. Pueri equum album habent.
   Pueri equum album ducebant.
   Pueri equum laetum ducebant.
   Agricolae equum laetum ducebant.

Parse Strings

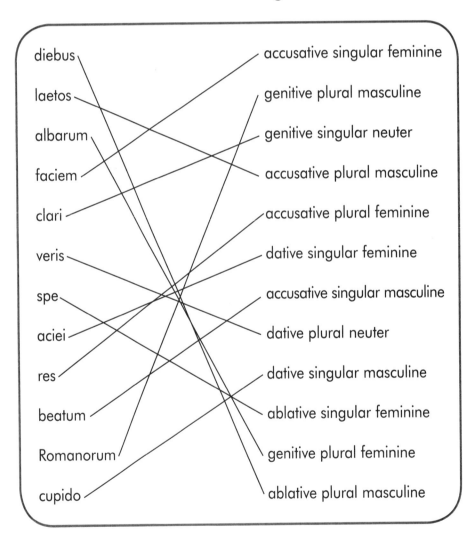

diebus   accusative singular feminine

laetos   genitive plural masculine

albarum   genitive singular neuter

faciem   accusative plural masculine

clari   accusative plural feminine

veris   dative singular feminine

spe   accusative singular masculine

aciei   dative plural neuter

res   dative singular masculine

beatum   ablative singular feminine

Romanorum   genitive plural feminine

cupido   ablative plural masculine

Match Up

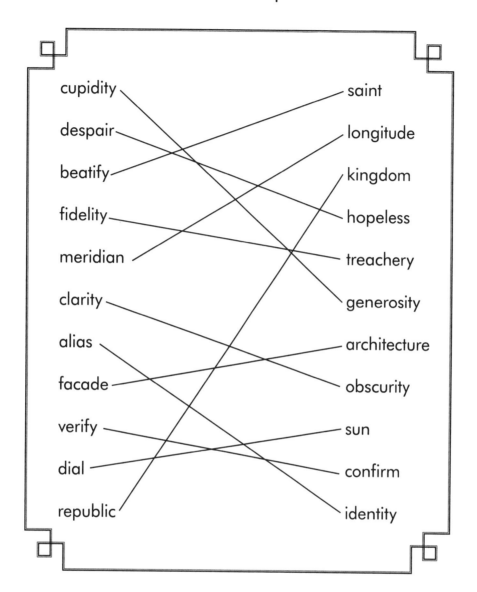

cupidity   saint

despair   longitude

beatify   kingdom

fidelity   hopeless

meridian   treachery

clarity   generosity

alias   architecture

facade   obscurity

verify   sun

dial   confirm

republic   identity

Vocabulary and Derivatives

LATIN	ENGLISH	DERIVATIVE(S)
A		
a, ab (prep. w. abl.)	from, away from	
acies, aciei F	battle line	
ad (prep. w. acc.)	to, toward, near	
adoro (1)	adore	adoration
adventus, us M	arrival, coming	advent, adventure
aeternus, a, um	eternal, everlasting	eternity
ager, agri M	field (agricultural)	agriculture
agnus, i M	lamb	
ago, agere	do, drive, act, treat	agent, agile
agricola, ae M	farmer	agriculture
albus, a, um	white	albino
alienus, a, um	foreign, unfavorable	alien, alienate
almus, a, um	nurturing, kindly	
altus, a, um	high, deep	altitude, altar
ambulo (1)	walk	ambulance
amicus, i M	friend	amicable
amo (1)	love	amorous, amateur
angelus, i M	angel	angelic
animus, i M	mind, spirit	animated, animal
annus, i M	year	annual, annals, anniversary
ante (prep. w. acc.)	before	antique
aperio (4)	open	aperture
apostolus, i M	apostle	
appello (1)	speak to, address	appeal, appellation
aqua, ae F	water	aquarium, aquatic, aqueduct
aquarius	The Water Carrier	
aquila, ae F	eagle	aquiline
ara, ae F	altar	
arbor, arboris F	tree	arboretum, arbor
aries	The Ram	
aro (1)	plow	arable
ars, artis F i-stem	art, skill	artist, artificial
audio (4)	hear	audition, auditorium, audible, audience
augeo (2)	increase	augment
auriga, ae M	charioteer	
aurora, ae F	dawn	aurora borealis
autem (adv.)	however	
auxilium, i N	help, aid	auxiliary
avis, avis F i-stem	bird	aviation, aviator, aviary
B		
barbarus, i M	barbarian	barbaric
beatus, a, um	blessed	beatitude
bellum, i N	war	bellicose, belligerent, rebel
bene (adv.)	well	benefit, benevolent
bibo, bibere	drink	bib, beverage, imbibe
bonus, a, um	good	bonbon, bonny

Latin-English Vocabulary

LATIN	ENGLISH	DERIVATIVE(S)
C		
cado, cadere	fall	cadence, cascade
caelum, i N	heaven	celestial
Caesar, Caesaris M	Caesar	tsar, czar, kaiser
campus, i M	field (athletic, assembly)	camp
cancer	The Crab	
canis, canis C i-stem	dog	canine
cano, canere	sing	canticle, cantata
capillus, i M	hair	capillary
capricorn	The Goat	
caput, capitis N	head	Capitol, capital, capitalize
caritas, caritatis F	love, charity	care, charity
carmen, carminis N	song	
casa, ae F	cottage	casino
caveo (2)	guard against, beware of	caution
cena, ae F	dinner	
centum	hundred	cent, century, percent, centennial, centigrade
centurio, centurionis M	centurion	
certus, a, um	certain, sure	certainly
Christianus, a, um	Christian	
Christianus i M	a Christian	
Christus, i M	Christ	
cibus, i M	food	ciborium
circum (prep. w. acc.)	around, about	
cithara, ae F	harp	guitar
civis, civis C i-stem	citizen	civil, civilian, civilian
civitas, civitatis F	state	civil, civility, city, citizen, civilization
clam (adv.)	secretly	clandestine
clamo (1)	shout	clamor, clamorous, exclamation, claim
clamor, clamoris M	shout, shouting	clamor, clamorous, exclamation
clarus, a, um	clear, bright, famous	clarity, clearance, clarify, clarinet
claudo, claudere	shut	clause, close, closet, claustrophobia
collis, collis M i-stem	hill	
contra (prep. w. acc.)	against	contradict, contrary, contrast
cor, cordis N	heart	cordial, core, courage
corona, ae F	crown	coronation
corpus, corporis N	body	corporal, corpse, corps, corporation
cras (adv.)	tomorrow	
credo, credere	believe	credible, incredible, creed, credit
crux, crucis F	cross	crucifix, crucifixion, crucial
culina, ae F	kitchen	culinary, kiln
culpa, ae F	fault, crime	culprit, culpable
cum (prep. w. abl.)	with	
cupidus, a, um	eager, desirous	Cupid, cupidity
cur (adv.)	why?	
curro, currere	run	current, currency, concurrent
custos, custodis M	guard	custody, custodian

Latin-English Vocabulary

LATIN	ENGLISH	DERIVATIVE(S)
D		
de (prep. w. abl.)	down from	
debeo (2)	owe, ought	debt, debtor, duty
debitum, i N	debt, trespass	debit
decem	ten	December
defendo, defendere	defend	defensive, defense, defendant
dens, dentis M i-stem	tooth	dental, dentist
Deus, i M	God	deity
dico, dicere	say, tell	dictionary, dictator, predict, verdict, contradict
dies, diei M (or F)	day	dial, diary
discipulus, i M	student	disciple
diu (adv.)	for a long time	
do, dare, dedi, datus	give	donate, donation, donor
doceo (2)	teach	docile, document, doctrine, indoctrinate
dolor, doloris M	pain, sorrow	dolorous, Via Dolorosa
dominus, i M	lord, master	dominate, dominion
donum, i N	gift	donate, donation, donor
dormio (4)	sleep	dormitory, dormant, dormer
duco, ducere, duxi, ductus	lead, guide	duke, duchess, abduct, aqueduct, conduct
duo	two	duet, dual, duo
dux, ducis M	leader	duke, duke, aqueduct
E		
ecclesia, ae F	church	Ecclesiastes, ecclesiastical
edo, edere	eat	edible
ego, mei (pers. pronoun)	I, me	
epistula, ae F	letter	epistle
equitatus, us M	cavalry	equestrian
equus, i M	horse	equine, equestrian
eram (imperfect of sum)	I was	
ero (future of sum)	I will be	
erro (1)	err	errant, erratic, aberration
et (conj.)	and	etcetera
etiam (adv.)	also, even	
Evangelium, i N	gospel	evangelist, evangelical, evangelism
e, ex (prep. w. abl.)	out of	exit, extra
exercitus, us M	army	exercise
exspecto (1)	wait for	expectation
F		
fabula, ae F	story	fable, fabulous
facies, faciei F	face	facial, façade
fama, ae F	fame, rumor, report	famous, infamous
femina, ae F	woman	feminine, female
fenestra, ae F	window	
fides, fidei F	faith, loyalty	fidelity, infidel
filia, ae F	daughter	filial
filius, i M	son	filial
finio (4)	finish	final, finite

Latin-English Vocabulary

LATIN	ENGLISH	DERIVATIVE(S)
finis, finis M i-stem	end, boundary	finish, definite
fleo (2)	cry, weep	feeble
flumen, fluminis N	river	fluid
fons, fontis M i-stem	fountain, spring, source	font, fount
fortuna, ae F	fortune, chance	fortune, fortunate
forum, i N	forum	
frater, fratris M	brother	fraternal, fraternity
fructus, us M	fruit, profit, enjoyment	fruit
frumentum, i N	grain, crops	
fuga, ae F	flight	fugitive, refugee, fugue

G

LATIN	ENGLISH	DERIVATIVE(S)
Gallia, ae F	Gaul	Gallic
Gallus, i M	a Gaul	
gaudium, i N	joy	gaudy
geminus, i M	twin	
gens, gentis F i-stem	tribe	genitive, progeny, generate, gender
gladius, i M	sword	gladiator, gladiola
gloria, ae F	glory, fame	glorious, glorify
gratia, ae F	grace, thanks	gracious, gratitude

H

LATIN	ENGLISH	DERIVATIVE(S)
habeo (2)	have	habit
habito (1)	live, inhabit, dwell	inhabit, habitation
herba, ae F	herb, plant	herb, herbal, herbivore
heri (adv.)	yesterday	
Hispania, ae F	Spain	Hispanic
hodie (adv.)	today	
homo, hominis M	man	homicide, homo sapiens
hora, ae F	hour	horoscope
hortus, i M	garden	horticulture
hostis, hostis C i-stem	enemy	host, hostile, hostility

I

LATIN	ENGLISH	DERIVATIVE(S)
ignis, ignis F i-stem	fire	ignite, ignition, igneous
impedio (4)	hinder	impediment
imperator, imperatoris M	general, commander	imperative
imperium, i N	command, empire	imperial, emperor, empire, imperious
impetus, us M	attack	impetuous
in (prep. w. acc. or abl.)	in, on, into, against	
injuria, ae F	injury	injurious
insula, ae F	island	insulate, insular
inter (prep. w. acc.)	between, among	interior, intermission, intergalactic, interlude
ira, ae F	anger	ire, irate
Italia, ae F	Italy	italics
itaque (adv.)	therefore	
iter, itineris N	journey, march, route	itinerary

Latin-English Vocabulary

LATIN	ENGLISH	DERIVATIVE(S)
J		
janua, ae F	door	Janus, janitor, January
Jesus, Jesu	Jesus	
jubeo (2)	order, command	
judico (1)	judge	judiciary, justice
jus, juris N	right	jury, just, injure
L		
laboro (1)	work	laborious, laboratory
lacus, us M	lake	
laetus, a, um	happy, glad, joyful	
laudo (1)	praise	laud, laudable
lavo, lavare, lavi, lautus	wash	lavatory, lave
lectio, lectionis F	lesson	lecture
legatus, i M	lieutenant, envoy	delegate
legio, legionis F	legion	legionary
leo	The Lion	leonine
lex, legis F	law	legal, legislature
liber, libri M	book	library
libero (1)	set free	liberate, liberal, liberty
libertas, libertatis F	freedom, liberty	
libra	The Scales	
lingua, ae F	language, tongue	language, bilingual, linguistic
locus, i M	place	local, location
longus, a um	long	longitude
Lucia, ae F	Lucy	
ludus, -i M	game, sport, school	ludicrous
luna, ae F	moon	lunar, lunacy, lunatic
lupus, i M	wolf	
lux, lucis F	light	lucid, Lucifer
M		
magister, magistri M	teacher, master	magistrate, magisterium, majesty
magnus, a, um	large, great	magnify, magnificent
malus, a, um	bad	malady, maladjusted, malice, dismal
mandatum, i N	commandment	mandate, mandatory
maneo (2)	remain, stay	mansion
Marcus, i M	Mark	
mare, maris N i-stem	sea	marine, maritime, submarine
Maria, ae F	Mary	Mary
mater, matris F	mother	maternal, matrimony
memoria, ae F	memory	memorial, memorize
mens, mentis F i-stem	mind	mental
mensa, ae F	table	mesa
meridies, ei M	midday, noon	meridian
meus, a, um	my	
miles, militis M	soldier	military, militia
mille	thousand	mile, million, milligram, millenium

Latin-English Vocabulary

LATIN	ENGLISH	DERIVATIVE(S)
mitto, mittere, misi, missus	send	mission, missionary, emit, omit, admit, transmit, submit, permit
moneo (2)	warn	monitor, admonish
mons, montis M i-stem	mountain	mount
mora, ae F	delay	moratorium
mors, mortis F i-stem	death	mortal, mortality, immortal
mos, moris M	custom	moral
moveo (2)	move	movie, remove, move, movable
multus, a, um	much, many	multiply, multitude
mundus, i M	world	mundane
munio (4)	fortify, construct	ammunition, munitions
murus, i M	wall	mural

N
narro (1)	tell	narrator
nato (1)	swim	natatorium (indoor swimming pool)
natura, ae F	nature	natural
nauta, ae M	sailor	nautilus, nautical
navigo (1)	sail	navigate, navigation
navis, navis F i-stem	ship	navy, naval
nihil	nothing	
nimbus, i M	cloud	
nix, nivis F	snow	
nomen, nominis N	name	nominate, noun, nominative
non (adv.)	not	nonsense
nos, nostri (pers. pronoun)	we, us	
novus, a, um	new	novel, novice, innovate, renovate
nox, noctis F i-stem	night	nocturnal, equinox
numquam (adv.)	never	
nunc (adv.)	now	
nuntius, i M	message, messenger	announce, pronounce

O
occupo (1)	seize	occupy, occupation
octo	eight	October
oculus, i M	eye	ocular, binocular
oppidum, i N	town	
opus, operis N	work, deed	operator, operation
orator, oratoris M	speaker, orator	orator, oratorio, oratory
orbis, orbis M i-stem	world, orbit, circle	orbit
ordo, ordinis M	order, rank	order, ordain
oro (1)	pray, speak	oratory, orator
os, oris N	mouth	oral, orifice
ovis, ovis F i-stem	sheep	

Latin-English Vocabulary

LATIN	ENGLISH	DERIVATIVE(S)
P		
panis, panis M i-stem	bread	pantry, companion
paro (1)	prepare	preparation
pars, partis F i-stem	part	particle, particular, partial
parvus, a, um	small	
passio, passionis F	suffering	passion
pastor, pastoris M	shepherd	pastoral
pater, patris M	father	paternal, patrician
patria, ae F	fatherland, country	patriot, patriotic
pax, pacis F	peace	pacify, pacific, pacifier
peccatum, i N	sin, mistake	impeccable, peccadillo
pecunia, ae F	money	pecuniary, peculiar (from pecus, cow)
per (prep. w. acc.)	through	
periculum, i N	danger, peril	peril, perilous
pes, pedis M	foot	pedal, centipede, pedestrian, impede, impediment
peto, petere	seek, beg	petition
piscator, piscatoris M	fisherman	
pisces	The Fish	
placeo (2)	please	pleasant, placid
plenus, a, um	full	plenary, plenty, plentiful
poeta, ae M	poet	poetry
pono, ponere, posui, positus	put, place, set	exponent, position, postpone
pons, pontis M i-stem	bridge	pontoon
populus, i M	people	population, popular
porta, ae F	gate, door	porch, portal, porthole
porto (1)	carry	portable, transport, export, import
portus, us M	harbor	port, seaport
post (prep. w. acc.)	after, behind	posterior, posterity
praemium, i N	reward	premium
primus, a, um	first	primary, prime
principium, i N	beginning, foundation	principle, principle
proelium, i N	battle	
prohibeo (2)	prevent	prohibit
provincia, ae F	province	
proximus, a, um	next, nearest	proximity, approximate
puella, ae F	girl	
puer, pueri M	boy	puerile
pugna, ae F	fight	pugnacious, repugnant
pugno (1)	fight	pugnacious
punio (4)	punish	punitive
Q		
quattuor	four	quart, quarter, quartet (from quartus, fourth)
quid (interrog. pronoun)	what?	
quinque	five	quintuplets (from quintus, fifth)
quis (interrog. pronoun)	who?	
quod (conj.)	because	

Latin-English Vocabulary

LATIN	ENGLISH	DERIVATIVE(S)
R		
regina, ae F	queen	
regnum, i N	kingdom	
rego, regere	rule	regal, direct
res, rei F	thing	real, republic
respondeo (2)	respond, answer	respond, respond
rex, regis M	king	regal, Tyrannosaurus Rex
rideo (2)	laugh	ridicule, ridiculous
Roma, ae F	Rome	Roman
Romanus, a, um	Roman	
Romanus, i M	a Roman	
rus, ruris N	countryside	rural
S		
saeculum, i N	time, period, age, world	secular
saepe (adv.)	often	
sagittarius	The Archer	
sal, salis M	salt, sea water	saline
saluto (1)	greet	salutation, salute
sanctus, a, um	holy, saint	sanctify, sanctification, sanctuary
scientia, ae F	knowledge	science, conscience, conscious, omniscient
scio (4)	know	science, conscience, conscious
scorpio	The Scorpion	
scribo, scribere	write	scribe, describe, postscript, scripture, scribble
scutum, i N	shield	escutcheon (coat of arms shield)
secundus, a, um	second	secondary, second
sed (conj.)	but	
sedeo (2)	sit	sedentary, sediment, sedate
sedes, sedis F	seat, abode	sedentary, sedimentary
sella, ae F	chair	
semper (adv.)	always	
senator, senatoris M	senator	
senatus, us M	senate	
sentio (4)	feel, perceive, think	sensitive, resent, sentimental, sentiment
septem	seven	September
servo (1)	guard, keep	conserve, conservative
servus, i M	slave, servant	service, servant, servile
sex	six	sextet
sicut (adv.)	as	
signum, i N	sign, standard	signal, signature, insignia, design
silva, ae F	forest	sylvan, Pennsylvania, Transylvania
sine (prep. w. abl.)	without	
socius, i M	ally	social, society
sol, solis M	sun	solar, solstice, parasol
solus, a, um	alone, only	solitary, solitude, solo
soror, sororis F	sister	sorority
specto (1)	look at	spectacle, inspect, spectator, spectacular

LATIN	ENGLISH	DERIVATIVE(S)
spes, spei F	hope	despair, desperado
spiritus, us M	spirit	spiritual
statim (adv.)	immediately	
stella, ae F	star	stellar
sto, stare, steti, status	stand	stable, station, status
studium, i N	enthusiasm, zeal, learning	study, student, studious, studio
sub (prep. w. acc. or abl.)	under, at foot of	submarine, subway
sum	I am	
summus, a, um	highest	summit, sum
supero (1)	overcome, conquer	superior
super, supra (prep. w. acc.)	over, above	supernatural

T

tabella, ae F	tablet	
taberna, ae F	shop	tavern, tabernacle
taurus	The Bull	
telum, i N	weapon, dart	
tempto (1)	tempt	temptation
tempus, temporis N	time	temporal, tempo, tense
teneo (2)	hold	tenant, tenacious
tentatio tentationis, F	temptation	temptation
tergum, i N	back	
terra, ae F	land, earth	terrestrial, terrain, territory, Mediterranean
terreo (2)	frighten, terrify	terrify
tertius, a, um	third	tertiary
timeo (2)	fear	timid, intimidate
timor, timoris M	fear	timorous, timid, intimidate
toga, ae F	toga	toga
tollo, tollere	take away, raise up	tolerance
totus, a, um	whole	total
trado, tradere	hand over, deliver up	tradition
trans (prep. w. acc.)	across	
tres	three	trio, triangle
tu, tui (pers. pronoun)	you	
tuba, ae F	trumpet	tube
tum (adv.)	then, at that time	
tutus, a, um	safe	
tuus, a, um	your (one person)	

U

ubi (adv.)	where?	
umbra,ae F	shadow	umbrella
unda, ae F	wave	undulate, inundate
unus	one	unity, universe, union, unit, unique
undique	from all sides	
urbs, urbis F i-stem	city	urban, suburb
ursa, ae F	bear	Ursa Major, Ursa Minor
usus, us M	use, experience	

Latin-English Vocabulary

LATIN	ENGLISH	DERIVATIVE(S)
V		
valeo (2)	am well, am strong	valiant, valuable
vallum, i N	wall, rampart	
venio (4)	come	advent, intervene, event
ventus, i M	wind	vent, ventilate
ver, veris N	spring	vernal
verbum, i N	word	verbal, verbose, verb
veritas, veritatis F	truth	verity, verify, very
verus, a, um	true	verily, verify, verdict
via, ae F	road, way	viaduct, via
victoria, ae F	victory	victorious
vicus, i M	town, village	vicinity
video (2)	see	evident, vision, video
villa, ae F	farmhouse	village, villain
vinco, vincere, vici, victus	conquer	convict, invincible
vinum, i N	wine	vine, vineyard
vir, viri M	man	virtue, virile, virtual, triumvirate
virgo, virginis F	virgin	
virtus, virtutis F	virtue, courage	virtuous, virtue
vita, ae F	life	vital, vitamin
vivo, vivere	live	revive, vivid, revival
voco (1)	call	vocation, vocal, vocabulary
voluntas, voluntatis F	will, good will	voluntary
vos, vestri (pers. pronoun)	you	
vox, vocis F	voice	vocal, vocation
vulnus, vulneris N	wound	vulnerable, invulnerable

Key to Abbreviations

F   -   feminine gender
M   -   masculine gender
C   -   common gender (masculine or feminine according to the circumstances)

pers.   personal
prep.   preposition
adv.   adverb
conj.   conjunction
acc.   accusative
abl.   ablative